Minds,
Mothers
and Midwives

Minds, Mothers and Midwives

The Psychology of Childbirth

Joyce Prince

BA (Hons Psych) BSc (Econ) SRN SCM ABPsS

Principal Lecturer in Psychology, West London
Institute of Higher Education
Honorary Lecturer in Psychology, Institute of Obstetrics
and Gynaecology, University of London

Margaret E. Adams

DN (Lond) MTD

Senior Midwife Teacher, Queen Charlotte's Hospital for
Women
Examiner to the University of London, Diploma in
Nursing—Part B—Obstetrics
Examiner to the Central Midwives Board

Foreword by Anne Bent
SRN SCM MTD
Director of Education, The Royal College of Midwives

CHURCHILL LIVINGSTONE
EDINBURGH LONDON AND NEW YORK 1978

CHURCHILL LIVINGSTONE,
Medical Division of Longman Group Limited

Distributed in the United States of America by
Longman Inc., 19 West 44th Street, New York,
N.Y. 10036 and by associated companies,
branches and representatives throughout the
world.

First published 1978

ISBN 0 443 01553 8

British Library Cataloguing in Publication Data

Prince, Joyce
    Minds, mothers and midwives.
    1. Pregnancy—Psychological aspects   2. Childbirth
    —Psychological aspects
    I. Title   II. Adams, Margaret E
    612.6'3'019   RG560   78-40033

Printed in Singapore by
Singapore Offset Printing (Pte) Ltd.

Foreword

One of the most exciting and challenging tasks for any author must surely be to write on a subject for a particular profession when there is no similar existing work. This is exactly what the authors of this book have done for the midwifery profession.

The growth of knowledge in the biological and technological sciences and their application in the practice of obstetrics and neonatal paediatrics has tended to overshadow the progress made in the behavioural sciences. Midwives are increasingly aware of the necessity to understand the 'hows' and 'whys' of behaviour particularly in relation to childbearing, the interactions of the family, and the early behaviour of the newborn baby. This knowledge is fundamental to the midwife if she is to give the family the necessary care and support at perhaps the most crucial time in their lives.

Joyce Prince and Margaret Adams have gathered together in this book much of the work that has been done in the field of the behavioural sciences which is relevant to the midwife. They are well qualified to do this as they have worked together and both have considerable experience in the care of mothers and babies and in the training of midwives. They are fully aware of the needs of midwives and this book should go a long way towards meeting those needs.

London, 1978   Anne Bent

Preface

This book started several years ago when we were planning a short lecture-discussion course of psychology for pupil midwives. Until fairly recently midwife and psychologist have had neither interests nor concepts and language in common, and they have therefore had little occasion for communication with each other. Since the 1960s there have been some remarkable developments in the practice of midwifery and obstetrics. Discoveries about the abilities and perceptions of young babies have coincided with these changes. It is becoming increasingly clear that the areas of interest of the midwife and the psychologist are interlocked. Premature delivery, feeding difficulties, the non-thriving baby and non-accidental injury to infants, to take only a few examples, are recognized as being affected by psycho-social as well as physiological factors.

Psychologists are interested in behaviour and experience while midwives concern themselves mainly with normal (meaning physiologically normal) pregnancy, labour and puerperium. Physical and mental events cannot be separated rigidly for they affect one another intimately.

We have tried in this book to bring together ideas, theories, and empirical data which can help illuminate some of the ways in which psychological factors do affect child-bearing. We have coined a new word. The maternalizatum is our term for the whole continuous period from conception to the end of the puerperium. The terms pregnancy, labour and puerperium direct our attention, to some extent, to the differences between them. By the use of a single term we are emphasizing the continuity of development which goes into the satisfactory integration of the new child into the family.

We have spent many hours discussing how to translate technical terms and concepts into unspecialized language, and in learning how to see things from the other person's view point. We hope we have devised a book which will be of interest to all those who are concerned with mothers, fathers and babies. Because of its origins it is of prime interest to midwives though we hope that health visitors, doctors, social workers, district nurses and parents will also find something of value.

Much of the traditional role of the midwife has been abrogated by technical developments in obstetrics. These very developments have created the need for a deeper understanding of the psychological elements involved in reproduction. It is hoped that this book will not only be informative, but also help the midwife to modify and expand her own professional role, and to find new sources of fulfilment for herself and her patients.

The photographs were taken specially for the book by Margaret Adams. These photographs help to demonstrate a few of the aspects of behaviour which we have discussed in the book. They show a few of the many people whose lives we have been privileged to observe, and sometimes to share, at such an important stage. We are greatly indebted to them.

London, 1978   J.P.
                                                                     M.E.A.

Contents

Introduction

The decline in the birth rate and the effective control over reproduction has greatly increased the interest in, and the value of, each new baby. In the developed countries each child born has a very high likelihood of reaching maturity. It is therefore, of great importance that each one should be given the best possible opportunities for development. Advances in midwifery, obstetrics and pediatrics ensure the survival of many mothers and babies who might previously have perished. The active management of labour, which has been the source of much debate in both medical and public press, has solved some problems at the expense of creating new ones. Some of the new issues to be faced by mothers, and those who care for them, before, during, and after childbirth, are of a psychological nature. One of the effects of the technical advances in obstetrics is increased intervention in the biological process of pregnancy, labour and childbirth. Much of the behaviour which is important in the reproductive process is spontaneous and emotional. Many of the changes from primitive to advanced society have depended upon interference or control of spontaneity. Interference may however distort or change a smooth sequence of behaviour. The mechanisation of labour, and the fact that most babies are now born in hospital, means that there are many ways in which the whole process of childbirth and hence, the relationship between mother and baby is subject to interference by nurses, doctors, midwives, technicians and machines. Recent research throws important light on psychological processes at work in the formation of attitudes to conception and pregnancy, and of different cultural ideals of the maternal role. The many factors which influence maternal responsiveness, and the way in which babies develop emotionally, intellectually and socially, are relevant to both parents and also those with a professional interest in maternity and child health.

The first chapter reviews some of the changes of attitudes to mothers and babies and the social events which have brought these changes about. How mother and baby get on during their early days together is also discussed, as this is the time when a midwife's care or advice may profoundly influence the course of events.

One of the first questions usually asked about the new baby is whether it is a boy or girl. The second chapter discusses some of the differences between boy and girl babies, and how the child's sex affects behaviour towards him or her.

Feeding probably occupies more time, energy and thought than any other single activity for several months at the beginning of life, and certainly in the first two weeks. The chapter on feeding discusses the association of feeding with cultural attitudes and with some aspects of the baby's development.

There is always much discussion as to whether a baby can see, hear, think, remember and learn. Since the 1960s there have been a number of ingenious experiments and careful observations which throw new light on these traditional questions. These, as well as some of the many speculations that remain, are discussed in Chapter 4.

The discussion of neonatal abilities leads on to a chapter on physical and psychological development. It is important to try to tease out those factors in very early life which are transitory, and those which may have longer term consequences. It is also important to consider any possibility for reversing the effects of events which may have deleterious long-term consequences. A chapter on the handicapped child looks at some of the evidence available on this question. The birth of a less-than-whole child usually engenders intense emotions in the parents, and often in the professional workers involved as well.

One of the most upsetting events for families and professional workers is infant death. Mothers who have lost a baby often find they are bereft, not only of their child, but of help and support of those around them. Some of the problems involved in communicating about anxiety, depression and grief, are discussed.

Chapters 7, 8 and 9 are concerned with events which primarily affect the mother. Pregnancy is often a time during which preparatory changes are made, both in the personality of the mother and in family structure and arrangements. Pain is often not openly discussed at antenatal classes and we have discussed the need for more information on this subject.

Contraception, amniocentesis, genetic counselling, are relatively recent intrusions in the human reproductive pattern, and views about them become entangled with deeply entrenched attitudes and motivations. Similar difficulties are likely to be encountered in the antenatal period over issues about the termination or maintenance of the pregnancy. Wherever the opportunity for choice is introduced, responsibility is also invoked. This implies taking credit for a commendable outcome and being guilty about an undesirable one. The Women's Liberation Movement has greatly increased the consciousness in women of their own role in society, at work, and in families in relation to their husbands and children. The creating of a new baby means also the making of a new role for both parents. The role change is usually more acutely experienced by the mother than the father and some discussion on this is to be found in Chapter 7. The unsupported or unmarried mother often requires special consideration. A number of research reports show the considerable disadvantage to which the children of lone parents are exposed (Ferri 1976; Crellin, Pringle and West 1971; Report of the Committee on One-Parent Families 1974 The Finer Report). The Finer Report estimated that one-parent families form about a tenth of all families with children and that over one million children are involved. The Finer Report was concerned with families in which the father was the lone parent as well as those parented by mothers alone. Parents may be on their own for a number of reasons. This report does bring home the frequency of the occurrence. The earlier that help is made available the more benefit is likely to accrue to mother and baby. The chapter on labour discusses some of the changes that have taken place in this event in recent years and some possible consequences.

In Chapter 10 some factors which are likely to affect the family as a functioning social unit are considered. The paternal role and that of any other children have to be worked out. It is important that a family should have access to as many facilities appropriate for development as is possible. There are, therefore, some practical guides about facilities that may be available and specialist organisations which deal with particular problems, as well as an introduction to some of the more complex factors involved in the network of relationships in a family.

In the final chapter we speculate about the future of midwifery, of babies, their parents and society.

REFERENCES

Crellin, E., Pringle, M., West, P. (1971) *Born Illegitimate*. Slough: Bureau Books, NFER Publishing Co.
Ferri, E. (1976) *Growing Up in a One-parent Family*. Slough: NFER Publishing Co.
Report of the Committee on One-parent Families (The Finer Report) (1974) Department of Health and Social Security, London: HMSO.

1

Recent changes affecting midwifery

Private Willis in Gilbert & Sullivan's Iolanthe proclaims that 'Every boy and every gal that's born into the world alive is either a little Liberal or else a little Conservative'.

It is an unusual, eccentric mother who enquires about her new baby's political inclination at the moment of his birth. Most mothers want to know first if their baby is 'alright'; having been reassured that the baby is healthy and whole, the second question is often 'a boy or girl?'

Midwives are privileged to participate in the 'every-day miracle' of birth. Their answer to the second question 'Is it a boy or girl?' is, generally speaking, a matter of reporting on the luck of the draw. There is as yet no sure way that the sex of the child can be determined, although some mothers who have had an amniocentesis may have some information about the sex of their child before it is born. Much of the midwife's training, skill and concern however, is directed to ensuring that mother and baby are as healthy as possible, and that their relationship together should be established harmoniously, while they are under the midwife's care. The immediate well being of mother and baby may affect their long term relationship, and possibly the long term development of the child.

Attitudes to babies, child bearing and birth vary considerably from culture to culture, and such attitudes also change over time in any one society. In this country, dramatic changes, first in the infant mortality rate, and then in the birth rate, have had an enormous impact on attitudes to child bearing. Two and a half centuries ago the Queen of England, Queen Anne, presumably with access to the best medical advice available at the time, had 14 children, none of whom survived infancy. There is no reason to suppose that this state of reproductive wastage was exceptional, as will be obvious to any casual visitor to a well established Churchyard. A midwife looking back from the second

1

half of the 20th century to any previous period in history, cannot but marvel at the changes that have taken place. In recent years there have been changes in the law relating to abortion, the advent of a nearly foolproof contraceptive pill, the practice of controlled labour, the Sex Discrimination Act, and an increasing number of employed women. Changed attitudes have helped to bring these events about, but the events themselves presage further changes of attitude to mothers, babies and families. What Professor of Gynaecology would now open a lecture, as Somerset Maugham records happened at St. Thomas' Hospital in 1894 with 'Gentlemen, woman is an animal that micturates once a day, defaecates once a week, menstruates once a month and parturates once a year'. Parturition in such circumstances was unlikely to be invested with the concern and emotional intensity which it is currently accorded! The high birth rate, high infant mortality and Sarah Gamp all belong together in a society where individuals had little opportunity to exert influence or control over their lives or their reproduction. The establishment of midwifery as a highly skilled profession, reflects the social and medical changes which resulted in a fall in both the birth and infant mortality rates. *Laissez-faire* attitudes to birth and babies changed to those of care and concern. It was not until 1902 that the first antenatal bed (one only) was endowed in Edinburgh. The midwife changed in function from the person being 'with the wife' at childbirth, to a person properly educated and trained to understand the requirements for a healthy pregnancy, labour and puerperium. In this role she has been expected to be competent in detecting, and as far as possible preventing, anomalies and abnormalities, to take advantage of medical progress and to help the mother adapt to and manage her new baby.

Since the late 1960s there have been widespread changes in the care of women during labour. These changes have included more frequent induction and acceleration of labour, mechanical fetal heart monitoring, fetal blood sampling, and more effective pain relief with epidural analgesia. At the Twentieth British Congress of Obstetrics and Gynaecology in July 1974, Sir John Stallworthy (Professor Emeritus of Obstetrics and Gynaecology at Oxford) said that it is not yet known whether 'office hour obstetrics' will increase the mental, emotional, and physical trauma to women . . . or 'whether it may actually increase hazards to infants by increasing the number of premature babies separated from their mothers in intensive care nurseries'. Widespread concern has been expressed both by members of the professions involved and by the public. Mrs Doris Haire, President of the International Childbirth Education Association, has described the process as 'a cultural warping of childbirth'. The Association for Improvement in the Maternity Services campaign against undue interference in the birth process, and against pressure being brought on women to ensure a hospital delivery. The National Childbirth Trust has submitted a report of 'Some Mothers' Experience of Induced Labour' to the Department of Health and Social Security. It makes a number of recommendations that more information should be made available to prospective parents in coming to decisions about the management of labour. It says 'We are of the opinion that investigation is needed into the long term psychological effects, not only of induction, but also of the active management of labour on the mother, the child, the relationship between the two and the effect on the family'. The report ends with 'The way we have our babies is an expression of human values in our Society for which parents and others, as well as doctors, are responsible'. The B.B.C. Horizon Team effectively brought the debate into the living rooms of the general public with a detailed controversial programme showing some aspects of modern methods of childbirth. The National Press have contributed to the discussion with articles on 'The Childbirth Revolution' (*Sunday Times Weekly Review* 20 October 1974) and *The Sun* started a week's series of articles with 'Assembly Line Babies'. At Queen Charlotte's Hospital there was a drop in the rate of surgical induction of labour from 26 per cent in 1974 to 19.3 per cent in 1975 (in 1971 it was 31.4 per cent). A possible explanation of this drop is that it resulted from patients anxiety enhanced by the Horizon programme mentioned above. How far the figures reflect upon the decisions of obstetricians and how far they are attributable to patients is not known.

Against the background of these technological changes the midwife's role is changing, and is likely to continue to do so, though not necessarily in the same direction as over the last decade. Home deliveries started to decline following the influential Peel Report in 1970. In this report the risks attached to home and hospital deliveries were compared, to the detriment of the former although this interpretation of the data has been questioned by Tew (1977). A survey by R.G. Law (1967) showed that with grand multiparae the neonatal mortality rate was unexpectedly higher in hospital deliveries. As controlled labour necessitates hospital delivery, the autonomous role of the midwife has largely given place to that of the hospital based midwife, who is one of a team of highly trained technical experts. Both the domiciliary midwife and her hospital counterpart, however, maintain their continuity of care and as such may emerge as the person to whom a woman may turn for advice and interpretation of complex information. In some hospitals, for example, women are given a choice as to whether they shall have an epidural analgesic or not. How should they come to a wise decision? It is not only a choice of reducing pain for themselves, but of how the baby is likely to be affected, and how the labour is likely to be concluded. (The incidence of instrumental delivery rises with the administration of epidural analgesia.)

Both epidural analgesia and forceps deliveries, however, continue to show an increase. There are many questions here that were raised by Sir John Stallworthy that yet remain unanswered.

Despite changes in obstetric practice, in the midwife's role and in social attitudes, the midwife's traditional interest in ensuring the health of the mother and baby and helping them to get on happily together, remain.

In the past it has been the concern of obstetricians and midwives to help mothers to have physically healthy babies. The perinatal mortality rate (P.M.R.) that is, stillbirths and deaths in the first week of life,

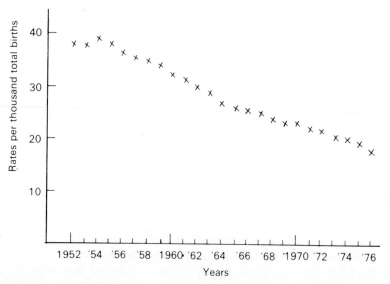

Figure 1.1. Perinatal mortality rate per thousand total births.

has been used as a barometer of success in this endeavour. The downward slope of the curve is cause for reasonable satisfaction (Fig. 1.1).

The chances of survival of pre-term, small for dates and sick babies have been improved and their morbidity reduced by the use of special care and incubator nursing. More recently, tests in the antenatal period of the Lecithin/Sphingomyelin ratio have reduced the incidence of respiratory distress syndrome (RDS) although this test is not yet used in all hospitals. In spite, however, of these advances, there does remain a considerable number of babies who spend their first few days in a Special Care Unit.

There are good reasons for believing that mothers who are separated from their babies at the beginning of the child's life, run the risk of difficulty in establishing a good relationship with the infant. With several species of mammal (sheep, goats, monkeys) the mother rejects the infant if the two are separated for the first three days of life. The rejection is the more severe if the mothers are both separated from their infants, *and* placed in a strange environment. If they are together for the first three days and separated subsequently, the mothers accept their babies on reunion. It is a common practice in sheep farming for the shepherd to 'graft' an orphan lamb on to a ewe who has lost her baby by putting the dead lamb's skin over the orphan. A study by Kennel *et al.*, (1974) in America shows that human mothers who have their babies with them all the time in the post-partum period, pay more attention to them, fondle and play with them more than mothers whose babies were cared for in accordance with the usual hospital routine, that is, where they spend a proportion of the day in a separate nursery. The difference between the two groups of mothers and babies was still apparent when the children were a year old. Human mothers are unlikely, at least when under surveillance in hospital, to refuse contact with their babies. They are more likely to express some unhappiness because they do not feel close to their baby. 'I can't really take to him', 'What an ugly little thing' are the kind of things they may say.

> Mrs Carmichael had her fifth,
> Looked at the job with repulsion,
> Said to the midwife 'Take it away –
> I'm through with over production'
> Louis MacNiece – *Bagpipe Music*

This is an example of frank rejection which in reality is seldom so baldly stated.

There are a number of reasons why mothers may not feel particularly attached to their babies. Whatever the reason may be, it cannot fail to be a source of concern to the midwife. Babies are highly valued and families are generally carefully planned. There is accumulating evidence that the baby who fails to elicit a mothering response, may be at risk in regard to his emotional, social and intellectual development and possibly his physical well-being. There is a higher incidence of non-accidental injury to babies who have been cared for during their early days in Special Care Units. Mothers who came to trial for neglect, cruelty or the killing of their young children, sometimes say that they never had much feeling for the victim, although other children in the family may be satisfactorily cared for. The occasional failure of the mothering response is nothing new. The tradition of the *changeling* child stems from the experience that mother and child seemed not to belong together in the normal way. Throughout history societies have tacitly approved a variety of methods of disposing of unwanted and uncared for babies, from exposure to feeding them ground glass or gin.

The changed attitudes to babies and young children make our response to such events one of very great concern, and make the midwife's role in helping the mother who may be at risk, a crucial one. She is in a central position from which to observe how the infant's behaviour affects the mother, how the mother's behaviour affects the child, and she must also be aware of how her own attitudes may affect them both. For example, in helping a new mother with breast feeding the midwife may be able to teach patience by example, as well as providing practical guidance.

It has been fashionable for some years past to consider a baby as a somewhat passive creature to whom things are done. Any problems that arise which make the baby difficult to manage, for example, sleeping or feeding problems, have been thought to originate with mother, who, it is argued, must be mishandling him. What this mishandling consists of is usually not clearly specified. There has been a lot of research in the past ten years or so, which might call these ideas into question. A normal newborn baby probably has much more individuality than has often been recognised.

At birth it is the usual practice in this country for a midwife or doctor to grade the baby on a number of characteristics to produce a composite Apgar score. Heart rate, respiration, muscle tone, reflex responsiveness and skin colour are each rated on a three point scale (0,

1 or 2) one minute and five minutes after birth. The maximum score is 10 but a score of 8 or over is considered to indicate a good condition. The Apgar score was originally devised for an assessment of asphyxia, so it could be treated more promptly. It has also proved useful in studies of the development of behaviour. Very low Apgar scores have been found to be related to mental retardation as well as physical handicaps, and intelligence test scores at four years have been found to be related to these Apgar scores. What is perhaps more surprising, is that babies with scores of 7–9, which are considered reasonably normal, do less well than babies with perfect scores, at the age of 3, 9 and 13 months on a test of attentiveness. The children with Apgar scores of 10 concentrated longer and better on pictures they were given to look at. The ability to concentrate plays a very important part in learning and in intellectual development, and this study is important in showing how fairly small differences in condition at birth can affect the individual's development, at any rate within the first year of life (Lewis *et al.* 1967).

In 1973 a Neonatal Behavioural Assessment Scale was published in

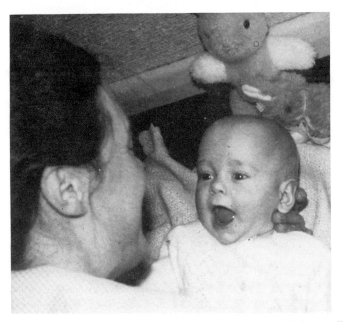

Figure 1.2. Initial stages of communication are made by mother and child responding to subtle signals.

this country. The author, T.T. Berry Brazelton, an American paediatrician at Harvard Medical School, says in his introduction 'The
Neonatal Behavioural Assessment Scale allows for an assessment of
the infant's capabilities along dimensions that we think are relevant to
his developing social relationships'. It is plain that some babies within
a day or two of birth are quite active in initiating and sustaining some
kind of social behaviour. This is done by subtle *signals* such as head
turning, eye movements and hand movements. The observant and
responsive mother reacts to these signals without being entirely aware
of doing so, and thus the foundations for communication are laid,
upon which a relationship of understanding can be built (Fig. 1.2).
Much of the early behaviour of this bond between mother and baby
happens too fleetingly and subtley for a human observer to be aware of
it. Slowed videotape recording make this awareness possible
(Richards 1971). From such recordings it is clear that some mothers
can be too active and they then interrupt the baby's sequence of
signalling behaviour. In the way that some people who talk rather a lot
do not seem to be able to listen to what another person is saying, so
some mothers seem to push their side of the communication without
giving the baby the opportunity to play his part. This event does seem
to be experienced as frustrating for both mother and child.

Since the early 1960s there has been an increasing number of studies
of the behaviour of mothers and their new babies. From these studies
it is apparent that features of the infant can affect this behaviour.
Perhaps the most obvious thing is his state of alertness. It is certainly
not the case that babies are either asleep or in need of food, as has been
thought. Brazelton, in his Neonatal Behavioural Assessment Scale
mentioned above, proposes distinguishable states which are:-

Deep sleep
Light sleep
Drowsy or semi-dozing
Alert, but with minimum motor activity
Eyes open with considerable motor activity
Crying

Anyone having the care of new babies for prolonged periods will be
well aware that there are considerable differences between one baby
and the next, both in how much time he spends in the various states,
and how they are distributed over the 24 hours. The amount of time
babies spend asleep has probably been overestimated. In one study the

amount of time over 24 hours in the alert but quiet state varied from 4 per cent to 37 per cent of the total time. Perhaps the states which concern mothers and midwives most, are sleeping and crying. Night waking is accepted in the first week or so of life, but it is generally believed that the baby should settle to the normal diurnal cycle sooner or later. If night waking extends beyond about three months the assumption is often that the baby is being mishandled. An enquiry by Richards (1975) into the sleeping habits of babies calls this traditional view in question. Richards has observed two important features. One is that sleep problems are quite common, and the second is that the tendency to wake is an individual characteristic of the child which persists during the first year of life and often longer.

In the neonatal period, amounts of sleeping and crying are important and so is the time at which these activities occur. Two babies may cry for the same length of time during 24 hours. The effect this has on their mother will depend quite a lot on the time at which it occurs. In Richards' study mentioned above, the babies who throughout their first year of life were troubled by night waking, had, as neonates, cried more and had been more irritable and fussy. These mothers had had significantly longer labours, and the babies were slower to cry and establish regular breathing at birth. This points to a fairly persistent individual characteristic of the child. From a practical point of view, advice to parents faced with a night waking child, may have to take into account the possibility that the problem is to be lived with rather than solved. This, of course, is a difficulty which extends far beyond the neonatal period, but may become apparent in the early days. If, as is suggested by evidence of recent studies, night waking and crying is a pattern of behaviour often resistant to alteration, perhaps mothers can be helped to plan their lives around that fact, rather than being allowed to feel guilty by the suggestion that they are mishandling their babies. Practical guidance on such a matter is more likely to be sought from the health visitor or general practitioner than from the midwife. A friend of one of the writers, who had dizygotic twins, one of whom was a night waker for over fifteen months, altered her own sleep pattern to accommodate this fact. Her husband was able to care for the other twin of more regular habit and the elder daughter, first thing in the morning until the other two members of the family emerged refreshed! This was a more realistic way of coping, rather than trying endless manoeuvres to induce the child to change his life style. It is clear that many of them do not. They refuse to accept the long held adult view that babies are passive and malleable. In some respects they may be susceptible to environmental pressures, but it is important to try to tease out which aspects of their behaviour are fairly individualistic, and which ones are amenable to outside influences.

States of alertness are one of the features of the newborn which depend quite heavily on 'inside' or 'biological' factors, and neither the states nor the timing of them seem to be easy to influence externally. If you watch a baby in deep sleep you will notice that occasionally he seems to *startle* quite spontaneously. Nothing moved his cot, there was no loud noise to disturb him – the disturbance comes from within. Such a startle will sometimes change his sleep from deep to light. The large majority of babies are more responsive to internal than to external changes. Many can sleep through a great deal of noise and movement without stirring, but if they are roused by homeostatic imbalance, they are likely to become more and more alert. In the normal newborn this imbalance is usually very simply accounted for by hunger, for which the baby has a very effective communication system! A small proportion of babies do seem to be relatively sensitive to external stimuli. It is not yet clear whether these early differences have a long term significance.

One of the important features of the Brazelton test is the assessement it makes of a young baby's ability to ignore outside stimuli. It is important for any living creature to select the signals from the outside world that are significant. Consider yourself walking down the High Street. It is unlikely that you will startle and run from every motor vehicle you hear or see, as you have become entirely accustomed to the noise; so accustomed indeed that you are unlikely even to be aware of it. A novel stimulus may immediately rivet your attention, however, – a pavement musician or the smell of roasting coffee reaches your conscious mind immediately. The process by which we manage to ignore oft-repeated stimuli is called habituation, and the decreasing response is known as response decrement. In the Brazelton test the baby's ability to cut out stimuli successfully is measured in several ways. For example to assess the child's response decrement to light, a torch is shone on the sleeping baby's face. He shows some response – by screwing up his face, perhaps moving his head or body. The light is then put off for a few seconds and shone again on his face. This procedure is followed ten times. Babies vary very considerably in their ability to ignore such an irritating disturbance. Some will still be responding to the light after ten trials while others *cut-out* after only two or three. The latter seem to be saying 'There is no harm from that light – I need take no notice'. Those who continue to respond seem to be saying 'I'm still not sure whether this is something I should pay attention to for my own good'. There are high correlations between response decrement to light, sound and pin pricks indicating that the ability depends on some general feature of the nervous system. It seems likely that the baby whose response decrement is fast, will be a relatively calm and placid baby who is fairly easy to manage. This quality will have a considerable bearing on his relationship with his parents. It is important to recognise that babies have very individual ways of responding to stimuli from within and without. Although it may be rather more convenient to live with a placid baby it should not be assumed that there is something wrong with one who does not settle so easily, or who wakes readily.

Feeding the new baby is of central concern, not only to mother and midwife but certainly to the baby, as he makes clear at fairly regular intervals. Despite increasing support of breast feeding by paediatricians a relatively small proportion of mothers maintain lactation for longer than a month.

There is a well known correlation between successful breast feeding and the social class of the mother. (Newson & Newson 1963; Sweit, Fayers & Cooper 1977) Middle class mothers are not only more motivated (in that they plan to breast feed) but they also continue to do so longer. Marketers of infant foods produce very appealing advertisements, as a glance through any woman's magazine will confirm; there is little persuasion on such a scale in favour of breast feeding. There are quite strong psychological pressures which associate breast feeding with immodesty. The breast is a sex symbol and to expose the breast is interpreted as an act of blatant sexual behaviour. If the pressures are to be withstood, the establishment of lactation and feeding have to be associated with satisfaction. The most important satisfaction is a contented baby. (The mother may be concerned about the contentment of the midwife for the short period she is under her care, but this concern may be short lived!) In one study done with a group of mothers delivered at home, the mothers were asked to keep a detailed account of what happened during the first 10 days (Richards & Bernal 1972). It was found that breast feeding mothers fed their babies more frequently (mean number of feeds per 24 hours for breast feeders was 6.6 and for bottle feeders 6.0). The professional advice given to these mothers was that they should feed 4 hourly, missing the very early morning feed. This would have meant 5 feeds per 24 hours. As human milk has a fairly low protein content, it is probable that breast fed babies need feeding rather more frequently. Different species of nonhuman mammals produce milk that varies over a wide range in its protein and other solid content. Those animals with dilute milk suckle their offspring more or less continuously, while those, like the rabbit, who have very concentrated milk, feed their offspring as infrequently as every 24 hours. Human milk is at the dilute end of the range, and is therefore thought to be more suitable for frequent, if not continuous, feeding. In some cultures babies are carried in such a way that they can be suckled at any time. The mother carries the child in a sling in such a manner that her nipple and his mouth are never far apart. In the study already mentioned it was found that crying was more frequent with breast fed babies (Richards & Bernal 1972). Those mothers who continued breast feeding successfully were more likely to respond to the crying by giving another feed, rather than any other kind of intervention. This points to the willingness of successful breast feeding mothers to adapt their routine to the needs of the child, rather than to stick to some preconceived plan. The mothers who, during the antenatal period, had expressed somewhat rigid views about feeding schedules, relinquished attempts at breast feeding fairly readily. The mother's readiness to adapt her routine may be influenced by factors occurring immediately after birth. A recent study (Sosa *et al.* 1976) in Guatamala shows that when mother and baby are left alone with skin to skin contact for 45 minutes immediately after birth, breast feeding is continued for longer than with mothers who are subject to the normal hospital routine of separation immediately after birth.

Inappropriately made up feeds have recently been implicated in cot deaths and hypernatraemic dehydration (Taitz & Bayers 1972; Macauley & Watson 1967). There is also evidence that some mothers continually ignore or defy attempts by health visitors to persuade them to make up feeds correctly. This adds to the catalogue of risks to which the bottle fed baby is exposed, and puts a considerable onus on the midwife to help a mother find satisfaction in breast feeding in the first two weeks of the baby's life. Despite the positive views held by the midwife about breast feeding, she may find herself up against some deep laid antagonisms against breast feeding and against accepting babies as they are. She needs a positive attitude to breast feeding herself, and then the time to spend quietly and unhurriedly with the new mother. In hospital the rapid turnover of patients may militate against this. Pupil midwives and nurses in hospital often lack the experience to help; domiciliary confinements and early transfer home help the mother to greater success.

Before artificial milk was available babies of the middle and upper classes were farmed out to wet nurses, and breast feeding was associated with a mean and lowly social position. Montaigne, the 16th century French writer, had this to say 'I cannot abide that passion for caressing newborn children which have neither mental activities nor recognisable bodily shape by which to make themselves lovable, and I have never willingly suffered them to be fed in my presence'. The practice of swaddling, common in 17th century England involved binding the infant to a board which was then hung on the wall. Revulsion at many cruel treatments of infants and children is a sensibility recently acquired, and the midwife who can succeed in helping a mother to form a positive approach to breast feeding has to contend with some well established negative attitudes.

Feeding involves more than the baby's ingestion of food. It is an activity between mother and child which signifies important features of their relationship together. We have already mentioned the evidence showing that the mother who is willing to adapt her routine to the demands of the baby, is the more likely to be successful with breast feeding.

It is very difficult, if not impossible to breast feed a baby without being in close physical contact with it! In 1966, Harry and Margaret Harlow, two American psychologists, reported on an experiment they had carried out (Harlow & Harlow 1966). They had reared some Rhesus monkey babies with two mother models. One model was made of wire and the other model was covered in terry towelling. Half the monkeys received milk from the wire mother and half from the towelling mother. The two mothers quickly proved to be physiologically equivalent. Monkeys in the two groups drank the same amount of milk and gained weight at the same rate. The two 'mothers' proved, however, to be by no means psychologically equivalent. Records made automatically, showed that both groups of infants spent far more time climbing and clinging to their cloth covered mother than they did to their wire covered mother. They also ran to the cloth covered mother when they were frightened. In fact, they seemed to have grown to love the terry towelling one, who provided comfort but were quite unattached to the wire one even though it provided food. These now famous experiments by the Harlows have some implications for human beings. Contact-comfort, Harlow has argued, is an essential precursor of attachment which forms the basis for a loving relationship.

The need for attention is perhaps the most compelling human need, which is especially apparent in the very young. Whether close physical contact is the most rewarding attention for *all* human babies is open to question. Some babies are very cuddly and seem to mould themselves to the adult body who holds them. Others, however, rather resist this close contact and hold themselves rigidly. In a study by Schaffer & Emerson (1964) the behaviour of young babies and their mothers was observed carefully. They were all normal caring and responsive mothers and normal full term babies. It was observed that the babies had characteristic ways of responding to close physical contact. Some clearly loved it; others looked rather uncomfortable. Mothers too, had characteristic ways of dealing with their babies. Some were very much more inclined than others to pick them up, to cuddle them and hold them physically close. These were described as 'handling mothers'. Others were more inclined to speak to, or look at, their baby, to touch him or hold him on their knee in 'non-handling' ways. In Schaffer & Emerson's study of 28 babies and their mothers, there were 11 handling mothers, nine with cuddly and two with non-cuddly babies. There were 17 non-handling mothers, ten with cuddly babies and seven with non-cuddlers. The cuddly babies who were mismatched got a lot of cuddling from another member of the family or the mother adapted her own behaviour and gave way to the infant's demand.

The two handling mothers of non-cuddly babies adapted but experienced some embarrassment later on when relatives were faced with the somewhat negative response of an otherwise friendly child when cuddling was attempted. The babies in this study were followed up and non-cuddlers were found to be markedly different in their general behaviour and development from the cuddlers. They reached their milestones of sitting, crawling and standing before cuddlers. The baby who resists the physical constraints of cuddling in the neonatal period may emerge as the individual who, from earliest days is characterised by vigorous independence. It is important to be clear that an apparent dislike of cuddling does not mean a dislike of attention. The observant and responsive mother can engage in other means of contact. The *'en face'* position, for example, where the mother holds the baby away from her but looks into his face may be a manoeuvre a mother adopts to deal with a non-cuddler (Fig. 1.3).

Babies, like other human beings not only like and need attention,

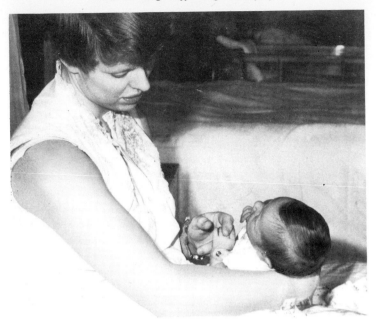

Figure 1.3. Mother making contact with a non-cuddly baby.

but pay attention as well. Periods of alert inactivity, that is, when the infant is fully awake, but quiet, are probably more frequent than is generally supposed. Kleitman (1963) in his evolutionary theory of sleep and wakefulness classified wakefulness into two types: that of necessity and that of choice. Wakefulness of necessity refers to conditions that are initiated by discomfort, such as hunger, cold and bowel discomfort. The periods of wakefulness by choice undoubtedly get longer with maturation, but they are present in normal newborns. A study by Wolff (1965) showed that in the first week of life of ten normal newborn bottle-fed babies, 11 per cent of the time was spent in alert inactivity. This increased to 21 per cent by the fourth week. During periods of alert inactivity the baby's eyes are open, and capable of conjugate eye movements. Some babies become alert and scan the surroundings when they are held to the shoulder for soothing.

Recent research at Boston University Medical School and St. Mary's Hospital, Paddington by Genevieve Carpenter (1970), with babies from one to eight weeks old, shows that from the first days, the newborn plays an active role in selecting the features of its environment to which it will attend. As early as two weeks of age the babies respond differently to the mother's face than to models of a face.

Babies are not infrequently affected by drugs administered to their mothers during labour. The drugs take longer to be excreted by the baby than by the adult, and so the baby may be sedated and unresponsive for a period at the beginning of life. This creates a state of psychological separation between mother and baby which may have an effect on their relationship. Babies who have been affected by Pethilorfan given to their mothers, have been compared with babies of mothers not given the drug. All babies were normally delivered and healthy. The drug-babies were slower to breathe and cry at birth, the length of their feeds was shorter and their food intake lower. They were sleepy and unresponsive and their mothers tried to arouse them by flicking their feet, or rubbing their legs. On following up these babies clear differences were found at 30 and 60 weeks. The drug babies were found to have fewer social interchanges with their mothers, and to be less involved in play activity. They also engaged in more self-stimulating activities, such as thumb sucking, than the non-drug babies. The long term effects remain to be seen, although it seems unlikely that a different path of development during the first year of life will not have some effect later.

The physical care of mother and baby has been vastly improved during this century. A whole and vigorous baby whose mother has difficulty in accepting him is at risk with regard to his long term development. It is undoubtedly part of the modern midwife's task to ensure that his right to a happy and fulfilling life is not jeopardised by problems created, or difficulties unobserved, in the first weeks of life. There are mothers of babies, indeed families, who need especially sensitive and skilled help to give them a good start. In the multicultural society which we have become, mothers originate from different cultural backgrounds. They come with a variety of attitudes, expectations and values about their family, their marriage and their babies which need to be taken into account. The very young, or the elderly mother, and one who lacks support of a husband or family have special needs. The woman who gives birth to a handicapped, or abnormal child, not only needs help to deal with her own disappointment, but considerable resources to help the baby maximise his capabilities. The mother whose baby dies is a very great source of anxiety; the course of her grief reaction can have radical effects on her family and may affect her attitudes to any subsequent children.

Generally speaking families are very carefully planned and high hopes are invested in each baby that arrives. The decline in the birth rate and in infant mortality has meant an orientation of public interest from child bearing to child rearing. It is now important, as perhaps never before, that every child shall have the best that can possibly be made available to him. This means not only the best in physical standards which we have come almost to take for granted, but the best in emotional satisfactions and opportunities for intellectual and social development. There is now abundant evidence that events before birth, and certainly at and immediately after birth, have an important bearing on these aspects of development. Midwives are especially privileged to be able not only to participate in 'the every day miracle', but also to be in a position to influence the satisfactory formation of the parent/child relationship so essential to the development of the mature adult personality.

REFERENCES

Carpenter, G.G., Tecce, J.J., Stechler, G., Friedman, J.S. (1970) Differential visual behaviour to human and humanoid faces in early infancy. *Merrill Palmer Quarterly*, **16** pp 91-108.

Harlow, H.F. & Harlow, M.K. (1966) Learning to Love. *American Scientist*, **54** pp 244-272.

Kennel, J.H., Jerauld, R., Wolfe, H., Chesler, D., Kreger, N., McAlpine, W., Steffa, M. & Klaus, M. (1974) Maternal behaviour one year after early and extended post partum contact. *Developmental Medicine and Child Neurology*, **16** pp 172-179.

Kleitman, N. (1963) *Sleep and wakefulness*. Chicago: University Press.

Law, R.G. (1967) *Standards of Obstetric Care*. A report on the North West Metropolitan Regional Obstetric Survey, 1962-1964 Edinburgh: E & S Livingstone.

Lewis, M., Bartels, B., Campbell, H., Goldberg, S. (1967) Individual differences in attention. *American Journal of Diseases of Children*, **113** pp 461-465.

Newson, J. & E. (1963) *Infant Care in an Urban Community*. London: Allen & Unwin.

MacNeice, Louis, (1973) Bagpipe Music. In *Oxford Book of Twentieth Century Verse*, p 395. Oxford: Clarendon Press.

Macaulay, D. & Watson, M. (1967) *Archives of Disease in Childhood*, **42** p 485.

Richards, M.P.M. (1971) Social Interaction in the first weeks of human life. *Psychiatria, Neurologia, Neurochirurgia*, **74** pp 35-42.

Richards, M.P.M. & Bernal, J.F. (1972) An observational study of infant—mother interaction in *Ethological studies of child behaviour*. Ed. Blurton-Jones, N. London: Cambridge University Press.

Richards, M.P.M. (1975) Unpublished lecture delivered at St. Charles Hospital, Ladbroke Grove.

Schaffer, H.R. & Emerson, P.E. (1964) Patterns of response to physical contact in early human development. *Journal of Child Psychology and Psychiatry*, **5** pp 1-13.

Sosa, R., Kennell, J.H., Klaus, M. & Urrutia, J.J. (1976) The effect of early mother-infant contact on breast feeding, infection and growth in *Breast Feeding and the Mother*. Symposium 45. London: CIBA Foundation.

Sun 17 February 1975 *et seq.*
Sunday Times Review 20 October 1974.
Sweit, M. de, Fayers, P. & Cooper, L. (1977) *Lancet,* i 892.
Taitz, L.S. & Bayers, H.D. (1972) *Archives of Disease in Childhood,* **47** p 257.
Tew, M. (1977) Where to be born. *New Society,* **39** No. 746pp 120-121
Wolff, P.H. (1965). The development of attention in young infants. *Annals of the New York Academy of Sciences,* **118** pp 815-830.

2

Boy or girl

'It's a girl'. 'It's a boy'. These words are the first spoken at many deliveries. Friends and relatives are informed, telephone wires buzz with *son*, *daughter*, and cards in either blue or pink are despatched. Interest in the sex of the new baby takes second place only to a concern for its health.

At all social encounters the sexual identity of the other person is a matter of primary concern. Birth is the first social encounter and ends several months of speculation about the baby's appearance, personality and sex. During the pregnancy and especially during the final weeks when the fetus is constantly making its presence felt, mothers spend a lot of time thinking about their baby, how they will look after it, what it will be called, where it will sleep, and so on. An important part of this forward planning is the sex of the child. Some have strong preferences or premonitions, while some are unconcerned about whether they have a boy or girl.

The antenatal period is one in which old established relationships are reviewed in the knowledge that a new relationship has to be made. If a baby girl is contemplated the mother may think of her as having some of the important characteristics and personality of her own mother or sister, and in her imagination, relive some of the relationships she has had with them. There are numerous indications that the course of pregnancy is characterised by changes in a woman's mood and behaviour. Some of these serve all important functions in helping her to adapt to her impending new role of motherhood. Taking on a new role means modifying already existing ones. A woman may, on one day imagine herself with a boy baby and wonder how such a child will fit in with the family. She may consider how her own mother and father will feel about him and how he will affect her relationships with other close relatives and friends. The idea of having a little boy can arouse feelings that have been associated with her father, husband,

19

brother or other important male figures in her life. On another day, the coming baby can be thought of as a little girl, and a correspondingly female set of relationships, feelings and ideas will be experienced. This review period may serve some important preparatory function.

As pregnancies are subject to increasing surveillance some careful enquiry into the effects of investigations, interferences, and the provision of information, on the psychological functioning of the mother is needed. Many mothers, having had an amniocentesis, vigourously reject the idea of knowing the sex of their child. Giving the mother information about the sex of the fetus may limit the mental explorations that are undertaken. We can only speculate as to how the thinking, fantasies, and day dreams of pregnancy affect the maternal response when the baby arrives. What is fairly certain, however, is that babies even before they are born are rarely thought of as neuter. Assigning a sex to the fetus may vary from day to day or it may be consistently 'Jane' or 'Robert' from fairly early in the pregnancy.

Producing a baby has much in common with roulette. Innumerable chance factors affect the outcome, and much of the zest is in the excitement and anticipation before the pointer comes to rest. If accurate predictions can be made, enthusiasm wanes. Extreme predictability and extreme novelty are both avoided by human beings so far as possible. The one is boring and the other frightening. Enough novelty to maintain interest, but not so much as to induce a feeling of insecurity, provides an agreeable situation for most of us. Sexual identity is so central to personality, that to know the sex of the baby before it is born may increase the boredom of the gestation period. This is clearly an area where speculation could, with profit, give way to some objective findings.

In any society where preferences of parents for boys or girls has been recorded, the result is consistently predictable. Boys have been, and are, universally more highly valued. There may be a good economic origin for this. In conditions where the population growth constantly threatens to outstrip resources, boys bring to the family the possibility of more labour and increased resources, whereas girls bring a potential for more children. There are innumerable sayings from all over the world which testify to the low regard in which girls have been held, for example 'May you have a hundred sons'; 'When a girl is born the walls weep'. A letter of Lady Frances Hatton to her husband in 1678 after the birth of their third daughter, reads, 'I am sure you will love it though it be a girl and I trust to God that I may live to bring you boys'. Until about a hundred years ago the Neapolitans would hang a small black flag from the window if a girl was born. This saved the neighbours the embarrassment of making enquiries.

The Agricultural and Industrial Revolutions, by greatly increasing resources, reduced the pressure of population and contraception in advanced countries has further reduced 'the problem. Attitudes, however, are passed from one generation to another, and can take a long time to change. A study in America in 1957 showed that the first choice of family for potential parents, is to have one boy and one girl. The second choice was to have two boys (Clare & Kiser 1957).

Parents who already had one child and were asked what sex of child they would have liked, modified their choice in favour of the already existing child. Husbands and wives of 173 families with a boy, and 192 families with a girl, gave the following replies (see Fig. 2.1). There is a

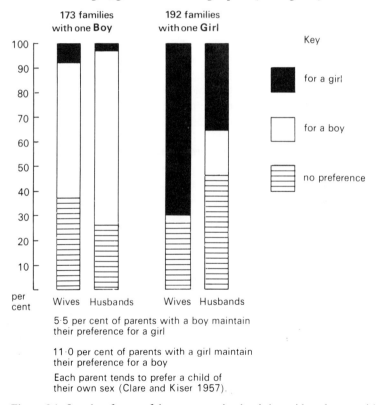

5·5 per cent of parents with a boy maintain their preference for a girl

11·0 per cent of parents with a girl maintain their preference for a boy

Each parent tends to prefer a child of their own sex (Clare and Kiser 1957).

Figure 2.1. Stated preference of those parents who already have either a boy or a girl.

marked tendency for parents to prefer a child of their own sex. The proportion of parents claiming no preference is also significantly higher when they have a girl. It is also plain that parents were more inclined to say they actually wanted the sex of child they had. It is more than likely that some of these parents changed their minds about their preference for a boy or girl after the baby was born.

There are in the urban industrial societies fairly strong pressures on parents to be good parents to both girls and boys. Strong personal preferences or dislikes are unlikely, therefore, to be acted upon. The mother who rejects her baby initially on account of its *wrong* sex, may need some very special help, but there are two things which ought to be remembered on the favourable side of this worrying situation. One is that affection of a mother for her child has a large learned component, and that if the mother can be supported by someone she trusts, the rejection may give way to a feeling of acceptance and affection. The other is that culturally there is now very much less discrimination against females, and also the distinctions between the sex roles have considerably blurred. Behaviour, attitudes and interests of boys and girls, men and women, overlap to an extent that was not possible in Victorian society for example. In societies where the sex roles are rigorously defined many people find their personality in conflict with the expectations others have of them. Florence Nightingale retreated to bed and invalidism to defend herself from the demands and expectations that her mother and sister had of her, that she should comply with the upper class female role of futile gentility. George Elliott and the Bronte Sisters wrote as men, because being intelligent or well-informed was incompatible with the female role at the time. Today boys and girls both play cricket and learn to cook, plan careers, go to parentcraft classes. In short, for both boys and girls, the range of acceptable behaviour is wider perhaps than ever before in any society. Although girls play cricket they play it less, and perhaps less well, than boys. Similarly, boys cook less than girls. There are attitudes, interests, aptitudes and behaviour that are found more frequently in one of the sexes than the other.

Innumerable psychological studies of men and women, boys and girls in USA and UK testify to the fact that there is a *modal* (most often occurring) personality for male and female. Males are more often aggressive, assertive, task orientated, ambitious: females are more often submissive, good with personal relationships, conformist, and verbal. Environmentalists have tended to explain such differences as a result of differential socialisation. Boys and girls are treated differently so they behave differently. The stories children usually hear present the girls as passive, sweet, and submissive, for example: Snow White, Rapunzel, Cinderella, and the boys as active, searching and dominant, for example: Tarzan, Lochinvar and Prince Charming. Boys and girls from babyhood are generally treated differently, have different activities which they are expected to imitate, and are encouraged to develop in different ways. The observations made by anthropologists of primitive cultures show that there is no inevitability about the development of male and female roles, such as exist in our own society. Margaret Mead (1933) describes three tribes, the Mundugamoor, the Arapesh and the Tchambuli. Both male and female Mundugamoor behave in ways which we might describe as characteristic of males; both male and female Arapesh have many qualities which in our society are connected with being female and, amongst the Tchambuli appropriate role behaviour is rather the reverse of our own. That is the women are more economically active and dominant, the men more submissive and retiring.

It is usually assumed that the physiological function is more or less fixed, and the environment may provide or withold opportunities for its expression or development. There is some evidence, however, to show that environmental factors can alter endocrine activity. For example, aggressive responses are known to be related to male hormone levels. The defeat of a male rhesus monkey by another male, is followed by a rapid fall in his blood testosterone level, ensuring that his next encounter will be less aggressive. Adult rats who are handled in babyhood have a different autonomic and endocrine response to physical trauma and fear, from those who are not handled in babyhood (Levine 1961).

The smooth running of society depends, to a large extent, on the fact that most people do what is expected of them. An experiment in which teachers were given the intelligence test scores of the children in their class showed how well the test scores predicted achievements. The only disconcerting feature was that the scores were muddled up so that the teachers had in fact been misled. They expected a child with a high score to do well and one with a low score to do badly. Interaction between teachers and children was such as to bring this about. The point we are making is that many traits and characteristics that are thought of as *fixed* may in fact be changeable, if not fluid. (Rosenthal & Jacobson 1966).

At present little is known with any precision about the way in which new born boys differ from new born girls. Girls are smaller and lighter although neurologically more mature. More boys are asphyxiated at birth and they are more susceptible to disease. How far this susceptibility affects brain development, and therefore behaviour, has yet to be explored. Indeed little is known about the way specific neonatal problems affect development of personality and behaviour. Certainly the general picture is that boys start at a disadvantage physically. A study by Moss (1967) suggests how biological and social factors may interact together. Boy babies cry more, perhaps because they are physically less strong and mature, and at three weeks of age their mothers pick them up more. This behaviour is gradually reversed. With year old children there is more close physical contact between mothers and daughters. It is possible that mothers become less responsive to insistent demands. Baby girls are more sensitive to tactile stimulation and to pain, but boys have better visual acuity.

Although there are a few sex differences at birth, the majority of dimensions on which infants differ show no observable sex differences. Girls are not more cuddly, boys are not more active, and so on. Babies in general vary in these and other behaviours but not on the basis of their sex. Work by Thomas *et al.*, (1964) suggests that differences in temperament are the most important factors in enduring patterns of behaviour.

There are, it is plain, traits and characteristics which are more commonly found in women, and others more commonly found in men. The influence of biological sex development on these characteristics varies. It is useful, therefore, to distinguish between sexual identity and gender identity. Sexual identity depends upon the possession of a male or female reproductive system. The large majority of biological males also feel masculine and behave as such. Biological females generally display feminine characteristics, so that their sexual and gender identity are consonant. Some little girls are described as tomboys, and women as having a masculine outlook; similarly the behaviour and attitudes of some men are more feminine. Gender identity is concerned with a wide range of attitudes, interests, preferences, ways of thinking, social behaviour and feelings. There are two possibilities only for sex identity (with the abnormal intersex condition making a rare third). Gender identity can range over a continuum from very masculine to very feminine.

At birth it is not usually difficult to determine whether the baby is a boy or girl. The judgement is normally made after inspection of the external genitalia. During the embryonic and fetal stages normal sexual development depends upon a number of factors. The human female has 23 pairs of chromosomes, one pair of which is, by convention, called the XX chromosomes – the male has 22 pairs and two unmatched ones, the X and Y chromosomes. The chromosome make up of the embryo is determined at conception and, providing the normal sequence of events occurs, the cell with XX chromosomes in the nucleus will grow to be a girl, and the cell with XY chromosomes to be a boy. Early embryonic development is the same for both sexes. Differentiation depends on an appropriate balance between the hormones androgen and oestrogen. Gonadal sex involving development of either ovaries or testes, is another essential feature of normal sexual development, and this is associated with the fourth factor, the internal reproductive system, and fifth the development of either the penis or vulva. There are five major biological jigsaw pieces which go to the making of boy or girl. They are chromosomes, hormones, gonads, internal reproductive system and external genitalia. Normally all these features, which together determine the sex of the infant, are consistent with each other, and sexual diagnosis is made on the basis of one of them, namely the external genitalia.

Very rarely the appearance of the genitalia may belie other parts of the reproductive system, or they may be neither clearly male nor female. The condition of intersexuality is fortunately uncommon. There are a wide variety of aetiological factors which can contribute to intersexuality, and by the time the infant is born an anomalous stage in development has had an irreversible effect. Treatment is therefore directed to ameliorating a permanent condition.

Authorities on the subject are generally agreed that there is no one feature by which sex can be diagnosed, and that an attempt to diagnose the *true* sex, in a case of intersexuality, is mistaken. Initial efforts have to be directed towards helping the parents in their decision about how the child shall be reared – as a boy or as a girl. After the birth investigations are likely to be carried out in order to assemble a picture of chromosomal, biochemical, and anatomical features of the baby. The assessment of the sexual status of the child is complicated by considerations of possible developments at puberty. The decision about the sex to which the child shall be assigned, cannot wait until puberty. The parents cannot treat their child as neuter, and to be uncertain whether to treat it as a boy or girl is to invite psychosocial difficulties.

John Money of John Hopkins Hospital has followed up and reported on the gender identity of four intersex babies. All four were genetic females with hormonal activity which had induced a hypertrophied clitoris looking like a penis. One was assigned as a girl and reared as such, and one as a boy. The other two were assigned only provisionally – one as a girl, one as a boy. The psychosexual development of the first two was in accord with their assigned sex. The one assigned provisionally as a girl was ambivalent about her gender identity and wanted to be confirmed in her feminine role. The boy provisionally assigned was similarly ambivalent and wanted to be confirmed in his masculine role. Recourse to a study involving only four children may give an oversimplified view, but there does seem to be a high level of agreement amongst researchers and practitioners dealing with the problem of intersexuality, that the sex in which the child is reared carries the greatest weight. That is, for normal psychosocial functioning, what matters is that feelings, attitudes, interests, ideas about the self, aspirations and ambitions should be consistently masculine or consistently feminine. As these aspects of psychic development depend on learning, it is important that the people from whom the child will learn are consistent in their own behaviour and attitudes. Money takes the view that experience in the first three years of life is of overwhelming importance in determining gender identity.

The parents will be the primary determinants of the child's gender role. If the baby is treated as a little boy, given boy's toys to play with and encouraged in boyish interests, he will develop a masculine gender role. A baby treated as a little girl, with pretty dresses to wear, an encouragement in feminine pursuits and interests, will develop a feminine gender role. Medical advisors would consider the extent of hormone support and the complexities of reconstructive surgery which would be necessary to promote one or the other role. It must be emphasised that the aim of any treatment and support is not to *make* the child either male or female in the physiological sense, but to make it possible for him or her to live a normal life free from the psychological difficulties associated with ambiguous sexuality.

In the last few years there have been a few well publicised *sex change* cases. These expose to public scrutiny the painful dilemma of people whose gender and sex role are incompatible. To have a body of one sex but the feeling, interests and aspirations of the other, is to live in a state of recurring, if not constant, conflict. Therapeutic endeavours are always directed to remodelling the sex organs or influencing the secondary sex characteristics of the body to accord with the psychic structure.

It is very important for the midwife to look carefully at the first examination of the baby, as any deviation from the normal should be noted, as it may mean that there are more internal abnormalities than external. Also, if the baby has a hypospadias it may need surgical treatment before school age, when it could be a social handicap. The midwife caring for the mother and baby whose sexual status is ambiguous has a variety of problems with which to grapple. A very rare form of intersexuality (adrenogenital syndrome) is associated with a condition requiring early diagnosis and treatment, as the excess adrenal hormones can lead to early death. With other conditions it may be considered medically advisable for corrective surgery to be done fairly early in life. In either of these cases the parents are faced with problems similar to those discussed in Chapter 7, about the ill or handicapped baby. Here we will discuss problems arising specifically from the baby's sexual anomaly.

There will be some delay while investigations are undertaken before any discussion about practicalities of the baby's upbringing can be embarked upon. Meanwhile relatives and friends will be anxious to know whether a girl or boy has been born, and this may be a painful difficulty in presenting the new baby to its siblings. This period of suspense can only add to the distress of the parents. There may be a number of accessory worries which parents are likely to harbour. They may fear for the general health of their baby or wonder whether it will be of normal intelligence. A common reaction in any such adversity is to look for somewhere to put the blame, and a mother in particular may be additionally distressed by finding some defect, real or imagined, in herself or her actions. Questions of the child's eventual sexual capabilities and fertility may also arise.

Sex and gender roles pervade deeply into many aspects of psychosocial functioning. Presented with a baby whose sex has not been assigned means that the parents are confused as to how to behave towards it. Mother-with-son behaves in important ways differently from mother-with-daughter. Gender assignation being so important socially, most people have strong feelings on the subject; some are repulsed by aberrant sexuality, and presumably no one would positively chose it for their child.

The midwife's role in the period following the birth, and before a considered medical opinion can be offered, is a supportive one. There will be many questions and problems which arise and cannot be answered. There are a number of studies done in general hospitals which show that the patients facing the most traumatic experiences have the least social contact with nursing staff. The natural response to a painful or embarrassing dilemma is to avoid it if possible. The mother of an intersex baby may be much comforted by finding that there is someone who can talk with her, and perhaps share some of the difficulties that arise in handling an intersex baby, and in dealing with relatives. It is fortunately unlikely that any midwife will have the opportunity of learning much from experience, as the condition is relatively rare. Ambiguity has to be tolerated for a time, by everyone closely concerned with the baby. This means that the midwife is in no position to advise the parents and, knowing this, she may feel inhibited in her discourse with the mother. This is perhaps a situation in which a parent will ask direct questions, not with the expectation of receiving an answer, but in the hope that someone will have the time and skill to listen sympathetically to how she views the problem.

The general public are very much better informed about medical matters than they were a few years ago. One consequence of this is a more general acceptance of the idea that medical and nursing professions do not know all the answers. To say 'we just don't know' is not a reflection of personal failure but an acknowledgement that medical science has not yet made progress in that particular direction. 'I don't know' may, of course, indicate a personal inadequacy as it may mean 'the information is available but I am not acquainted with it'. A midwife can always undertake to try to find out. It may be quite rewarding to enquire of the parents what they know and what their ideas are.

Once the medical course of action has been decided upon the parents are likely to gain confidence in their relationships with the infant. The possibility of rejection arises with any abnormal baby, but it should always be remembered that love for a child is very often a slowly developing process. Love at first sight, between a mother and her newborn infant, is probably not a particularly common event. One thing is plain, if the mother refuses to have any contact with the infant no affectionate feelings can develop. Initially her caring behaviour may be rather mechanical, and the relationship vulnerable. It is during that period that a midwife can provide an attentive ear, understanding mind, and an example of accepting behaviour.

Recent advances in genetics and fetology bring the possibility of choosing the sex of the offspring somewhat nearer. It is generally assumed, that should parents have the choice open to them more boys would be born. Etzioni (1969) of Columbia University has discussed the social consequences of an effective means of sex selection. As many aspects of social behaviour are sex related, an imbalance in the sexes would have far reaching effects on social life. Women are more average in a number of ways – there are more men at the extremes – intellectually, as subnormal and highly creative and inventive. There are more male criminals. Women are more conforming and many of them vote conservative in the United Kingdom and Republican in the United States of America. Etzioni claims that American women read more books, see more plays, and generally consume more culture than men. They are also charged with more responsibilities for child rearing and education. All social life is affected by the balance between the sexes. Any large imbalance would certainly reduce the prospect of a well ordered social life. In the United Kingdom a balance between the sexes of marriageable age was achieved during the 1950s for the first time since records started to be kept in 1811. The male habit of going to war periodically, strongly encouraged by the females, successfully reduced each generation of marriageable men. A monogamous society was thus supplied with an excess of young women to provide the labour force in hospitals, schools and the private homes of the more wealthy. The change in the sex ratio has affected these institutions, giving an added force to women's emancipation and altered the attitude of men and women to each other.

REFERENCES

Clare J.E. & Kiser, C.V. (1957) in *Social and Psychological factors affecting fertility.* Ed. Whelpton, P.K. & Kiser, C.V. 5 volumes New York: Millbank Memorial Fund.

Etzioni, A. (1969) *Science,* **161** pp 1101-1102.

Levine, S. (1961) The psychophysiological effect of early stimulation. In *Roots of Behaviour,* ed. Bliss, E.L. New York: Hoeber.

Mead, M. (1933) *Sex and Temperament in Three primitive societies.* New York: Morrow.

Money, J. (1970) Matched pairs of hermaphrodites: Behavioural biology of sexual differentiation from chromosomes to gender identity. *Engineering and Science* (California Institute of Technology) **33** pp 34-39.

Moss, H.A. (1967) Sex, age and state as determinants of mother-infant interaction. *Merrill Palmer Quarterly,* **13** pp 19-36.

Rosenthal, R. & Jacobson, L. (1966) Teachers' expectancies: determinants of pupils I.Q. gains. *Psychological Reports,* **19** pp 115-118.

Thomas, A., Chess, S., Birch, H., Hertzig, M.E. & Korn, S. (1964) *Behavioural individuality in early childhood.* New York: University Press.

3

Feeding

A number of decisions about the feeding of a new baby have to be made. Is it to be breast or bottle fed? Should feeds be given three hourly, four hourly, or on demand? If bottle feeding is the chosen method, which brand of milk will suit the infant? Who will make up the feeds and give them? To whom will the mother turn for advice, especially when things are not going well. Before reaching her decision she will be influenced in all kinds of ways, both subtle and simple, and the midwife is one of many people who has the opportunity to affect the mother's decision. But it is the mother, ultimately, who must find the answers to these questions in a way which she feels best suits herself and her baby. In some cases where artifical feeding is chosen and is incorrectly prepared there is a risk to the baby of serious complications such as gastroenteritis or hypernatraemia with the risk of brain damage.

There have been fads and fashions in infant feeding throughout history. Only in the 20th century has wider understanding of the biological sciences affected the choice, and in the last decade behavioural scientists have begun to explore some of the factors which affect mother and baby in this central aspect of their early relationship.

A review of feeding practices throughout the ages shows how closely they are related to the value put on infant life, and to general social conditions. Some of the problems and ideas which are being fervently discussed today have been aired recurrently from classical times onwards. For centuries doctors and moralists have been exhorting women to breast feed their own babies, although many mothers have avoided the task if the possibility has been open to them. Indeed babies' feeding bottles have been found by archeologists in parts of ancient Egypt, Greece and the Roman Empire. Some babies were dry nursed being fed pap or panada. These were mixtures of flour, bread or cereal and milk, or water. One authority writing at the end of the

17th century, complained that such food was 'More suitable for binders to bind their books than for the nourishment of infants', and, indeed, the numerous recipes that were available at that time look very similar to the recipe for flour and water paste! Needless to say, dry feeding was associated with 'summer diarrhoea' contributing to the high mortality rates. But by far the commonest alternative to the mother's breast milk, in cases where the mother was unable or disinclined to feed her own infant, was the wet nurse and this substitute was very widely practised. Some of the earliest wet nurses recorded were slave girls. The peak of popularity of wet nursing in England was reached in the 18th century, and there is little evidence that wet nurses have been much in demand since the mid 19th century. Jane Aitken, however, Chief Midwife to the Nurses' Charity at Guy's Hospital, has this to say in her *Textbook of Midwifery*, the fifth edition of which was published in 1934: 'A wet nurse is the best substitute for mother's milk'. She goes on to list seven essentials which must be sought in selecting a wet nurse. They are that she must be healthy, have firm, full breasts, well shaped nipples, a thriving child of her own a little older than the nursling, a good character, aged between 20 and 30 years, and she must also give up nursing her own child. As the birth rate was very low during the 1930s one can only suppose that there was no great supply of women able and willing to meet these requirements.

Exhortations, usually, but not always, by men, to mothers to breast feed their infants were often realistically accompanied by instructions on the selection of a wet nurse. As in Miss Aitken's *Textbook of Midwifery*, considerable attention was to be paid to the moral character of the woman. There were two reasons for this. The first was the obvious one that parents might have scruples about passing a child to the care of a negligent or malicious woman. The other was based on the strong belief that aspects of the feeder's character, temperament and personality, passed to the child in the breast milk.

What emerges from a historical perspective on infant feeding is that some of our 20th century problems are not new. It is plain that three factors which concern us today all have long histories. These three are: the reluctance of many women to breast feed their babies; the timing of the introduction of solid food into the baby's diet; and the idea that the breast feeding relationship has some long term effect on the child's psychological development.

Instead of breast milk, the natural sustenance for all mammals for the period immediately after birth, there are reasonable alternatives for human babies. A report of the Department of Health and Social Security in 1974 describes the United Kingdom as 'largely an artificially fed', or 'bottle feeding' nation. In 1946, 50 per cent of babies were being breast fed at three months old. The proportion in 1974 was an estimated six per cent. The reason for this decline is not difficult to understand. A brief review of the history of infant feeding indicates a common reluctance of mothers to suckle their babies. The twentieth century has added a number of reinforcements to this reluctance: the nutritional needs of infants have been scientifically studied; problems of hygiene in the developed countries have been largely overcome; commercial firms can produce artificial feeds for infants which are sterilised, nutritionally adequate, attractively advertised, and until recently, have been readily recommended by many health professionals.

The Midwives' Act of 1951 states that one of the duties of a midwife is to promote and encourage breast feeding. This was reinforced in a memorandum of 1963, and it is often only the midwife who has retained her interest in promoting and encouraging it. All but the most steadfast, however, have probably had some of their enthusiasm blighted by the general lack of support which the parents receive after the lying-in period. Indeed, some general practitioners, unable to spend the time in discussion and supervision of problems with breast feeding, have quite understandably often agreed with the patient that her milk was 'unsuitable' or 'too weak' for her baby, and suggested the bottle as a swift remedy. The doctor is often asked for advice that in previous generations the patient's mother, or other relative would have been available to give over the first few months following delivery.

The following quotation comes from the British Medical Bulletin of 1947: 'Expenditure on breast milk banks is unjustifiable because the preparation of cows' milk formula has now reached such a high standard of perfection as to render the provision of human milk, by this means, unnecessary.' Now, women who want to breast feed complain of the numerous disincentives with which they are faced in hospital. One mother writing in *The Times* (Neville, 1976) says that when she asked the nurse (variety unspecified) 'to take away the bottle as I was breast feeding, a look of awe crossed her face, she patted me on the back and said "Good girl", as if I were commendable but eccentric.' It is not unusual to hear it suggested that to try to persuade a woman to breast feed, risks engendering guilty feelings that she is

Table 3.1 Factors encouraging or discouraging breast feeding

Encouraging	Discouraging
General	
Expert advice favouring breast feeding	Expert advice
Encouragement from other members of the family (mother, husband)	Encouragement from other members of the family to bottle feed
Seeing other mothers breast feeding successfully	Seeing other people bottle feeding
	Advertising of artificial feeding
Early influences	
Breast feeding as seen in paintings and other representational art, by children	Now culturally accepted that babies are bottle fed—books, advertisements, television, as well as real life
Breast feeding mothers brought into parentcraft and sex education classes in schools, and to antenatal clinics run by midwives and hospitals	
Breast function	
Functional—lactation	Sex symbol—exposure associated with sexual anxiety
Economic efficiency	
Efficiency for mother of a very young baby requires observation responsiveness, patience	Efficiency in many jobs associated with time keeping, speed, precision etc
Education for woman's role	
Maternal role integrated into other roles. Suitable clothing for breast feeding in public, means of baby carrying	Women's liberation movement has concerned itself predominantly with women's role at work, as a sex partner, and socially, and has minimised or denigrated the maternal role

failing as a mother if she eventually is unable to do so. Good artificial milk preparations, invaluable for the baby whose mother cannot provide the nourishment, have been indiscriminately recommended, and persuasively advertised.

Some of the disastrous consequences of over-enthusiasm in the use of artifical food are apparent in the underdeveloped countries, where education, hygiene and domestic facilities are inappropriate for the proper preparation and care of artificial food.

Many psychologists have been uneasy for years about the effects of the unnecessary interference with a natural sequence of behaviour that bottle feeding implies. Until recently, however, there has been no evidence of a sufficiently precise nature to provide any influential argument. Recent evidence from behavioural science has more or less coincided with the information implicating artificial feeding of very young babies as a contributory factor in a number of sudden infant deaths. Hypernatraemic dehydration – leading to irreversible brain damage in some cases, and early and severe atopy (allergy) in babies in whose families there is a strong history of eczema, asthma or hay fever, are found more frequently in artificially fed babies than those who are breast fed. This incriminating evidence was that which instigated the Department of Health and Social Security report of 1974, *Present Day Practice in Infant Feeding,* and the memoranda which have followed.

The present position is that for a generation infant feeding has meant bottle feeding, and that in both the United Kingdom and the United States of America this has become the cultural pattern within which mothers relate to their babies. Convincing mothers of the advantages of breast feeding is difficult: it is usually easier to demonstrate a physical event than a psychological one and a weight gain is more immediately impressive than an improved relationship. *Present Day Practice in Infant Feeding* arose from a concern with the purely physical events (cot deaths, hypernatraemia etc.) the correction of which involves the changing of attitudes, ideas and of established patterns of behaviour, not only for parents but for some doctors, nurses, health visitors and midwives. The encouragement of breast feeding advocated by the Department of Health and Social Security report involves nothing less than a radical change in an important aspect of our culture. In Table 3.1 you will see in diagrammatic form some of the cultural features against, and in favour, of breast feeding.

Attitudes to breasts and breast feeding are by no means understood and so far little effort has been expended on exploring them. Many attitudes are learned in early life. Children 'pick up' emotional overtones to topics and adopt them as their own. Attitudes to immigrant groups, for example, are affected by parental attitudes. Children imbibe many of the opinions and beliefs of their parents without question. Some recent investigations show that if women believe that they were themselves breast fed they are more likely to do so. As there has been such a decline in breast feeding in the past three or four decades there must have been many women who were breast fed but who were more powerfully influenced against it by some other factors apart from their mothers. It would be interesting and of considerable practical use to know why some people are more readily persuasible than others. Regrettably there is little to help us. In Newcastle 200 newly delivered women were asked to list in order of priority the sources or people who had influenced their choice of feeding method. The results are shown in Table 3.2.

Table 3.2

| | % of mothers | |
	Breast feeding	Bottle feeding
Their own feelings	95	98
Husband	37	18
Mother	19	18
Hospital	21	7
Friends	20	7.5
Books	18	2
Media	12	2
General Practitioner	9	3
Health Visitor or Midwife	4	1

(Bacon and Wylie 1976)

In a similar study (also in Newcastle) with another 200 women, over half the group had made up their minds about preferred method of feeding before the pregnancy, and only 5.5 per cent decided after the delivery (Eastham *et al.* 1976). By far the most important influence is the woman's 'own feelings'. Feelings about particular issues are much the same as attitudes and it is reasonable to suppose that these have been built up as a result of life's experiences. Quite a large proportion of the group located influences in their family (mother and husband). Mothers who chose breast feeding are clearly open to many more influences or, which is more likely, are more aware of the influences, which affect their judgement. Breast feeding in the United Kingdom is class related. Social class 1 and 2 are not only more likely than Social class 4 and 5 to decide to breast feed, but also are likely to persist for longer (Newson & Newson 1963).

The likelihood that a woman having her first baby has had anything to do with a small baby, or has witnessed breast feeding, is remote. For most women their own first child is also their own first experience with a baby. A survey by Jane Hubert in South London published in 1974, showed how deplorably ill-informed a group of working class pregnant women were about conception, pregnancy, childbirth and child rearing. Although they attended the antenatal clinic they were inhibited in asking questions and did not understand much of what went on. From Jane Hubert's report it is clear that much effort put into antenatal education is frustrated by poor understanding. In many antenatal clinics a woman may see a variety of specialists who are likely to examine her with their own particular interests in mind. 'What is the size of the baby's head', 'Should an amniocentesis be done', 'Are there any irregular antibodies' and so on. It must be very difficult for some women to find the right moment and the right person to whom she can put her questions. Having found a midwife willing and able to listen, it may not be easy to frame the questions or express a worry fluently. The midwife, in her role of providing continuity of care has a key task of dealing with the whole person, worries, misunderstandings and all. This may mean translating the technical language and answering straightforward questions. Often, however, the experienced midwife will sense the hidden anxieties and allow the patient to discuss subjects that she feels the doctor may think unimportant.

Acquiring information is one kind of learning; there are others. The baby rhesus monkeys which were brought up with mechanical mother surrogates (see Ch. 1) developed well enough physically. When they grew up, however, their social and sexual behaviour was quite abnormal. They were difficult to mate and those females who did produce offspring had no idea how to look after them. They made cruel, neglectful and murderous mothers. They had had no handling, cuddling, restraining and touching from a parent in their own infancy and it is believed that the absence of this experience prevented them from behaving in a motherly way towards their own babies. It seems likely that human beings learn a lot from being cuddled, picked up and talked to as babies, which they can then pass on to the next generation. It has been found that newly delivered mothers who had been separated from their own mothers experienced more problems with their babies. They also had more marital problems (Frommer 1973).

The study already mentioned in Chapter 1, carried out in Guatamalan hospitals, shows how the contact effected, by putting the baby
naked on the mother's abdomen for 45 minutes after birth, and leaving
them alone together, affects lactation (Sosa *et al.* 1976). A follow-up of
these mothers and babies shows, amongst other things, that the
proportion who are still breast feeding at four months is higher than
those treated in the usual way in the hospital. Some writers have
suggested that there is a critical period immediately after birth when
the mother is especially likely to become attached to her infant. If they
are together for that period the mother will become observant and
responsive to her baby. If the time passes without the chance of this
learning taking place (as may happen if they are separated) there may
be difficulties for the mother in accepting the baby happily. The
findings from the Guatamalan study suggest that this critical period
may have some relevance to the establishment and maintenance of
breast feeding. In some parts of the world primigravidae 'borrow' a
baby and put it to the breast. This serves not only to prepare the breast
antenatally but gives the mother experience in handling and holding a
small baby.

The decline of the breast as a functional organ has coincided with its
cultivation as a sex symbol. The cult started in America during the
1920s and the sweater girls of the 1940s ensured that bust size, shape,
contour and measurement obtruded into the consciousness of all but
the most obtuse. Advertisers lost no time in exploiting the possibilities
of sexual anxiety inherent in the characteristics of the bosom. The
brassière which made its appearance around 1929 (there is some doubt
concerning the precise date) became an essential garment. The less
aggressively uplifting brassières have probably made life considerably
more comfortable for millions of women; a fact apparently overlooked
by the bra-burning wing of the women's liberation movement.

Many young women have become sufficiently dissatisfied with the
size and shape of their breasts to undergo plastic surgery, and fear of
losing their figure (meaning their breast contour) is a reason not
infrequently given for refusing to breast feed.

The displacement of sexual interest to the breast has in addition led
to potential jealousy sometimes openly expressed by the father of a
breast fed baby. Husbands, it will be remembered, were attributed
with considerable influence of choice of type of feeding by the sample
of women in Newcastle, mentioned earlier in the chapter.

The sexual connotations of breast size and shape have given a new meaning to uplift and vital statistics (e.g. Miss United Kingdom and Miss World are mainly assessed by their vital statistics!) They are now so closely associated with sexual anxiety that their functional properties are mentioned only in the specialised world of the antenatal clinic and lying-in ward.

There are formidable obstacles in the way of effectively encouraging breast feeding. Midwives, and perhaps more particularly, health visitors, are in a position to influence decisions about health education pamphlets, films, posters and content of talks to schools and mothers. The National Childbirth Trust have some educational programmes in which breast feeding mothers take part. The mother and baby could be presented as a breast feeding relationship in either word or picture. It has been an interesting fact that for years the firms which produce milk feeds for babies, have been at great pains to point out that their product is only second best to the breast! They were quick to appreciate that midwives, health visitors and paediatricians would then look more favourably at their products. The advertisements until recently however showed mothers bottle feeding their very attractive postneonatal babies. One film on breast feeding does present breast feeding, however, almost to the exclusion of the milk product which sponsored its manufacture, and presents it in an attractive and realistic way. It is most helpful for those women who have never seen a baby breast fed.

Better still, antenatal preparation might be helped by the incorporation of one or two mothers who have already had their babies. They could perhaps demonstrate to the apprehensive, the ease with which established breast feeding takes place. Often enough in hospital, the memorable scenes of the early post-natal period when attempts are being made to establish breast feeding are those of some distraught and tearful mothers and hungry frustrated babies. It is not surprising that, with this picture of breast feeding, many abandon the idea and quickly reach for the feeding bottle. If only it were understood that the 'third day problems' and, indeed the whole time in hospital, is quite atypical of the happy relationship which can develop between mother and baby when feeding is properly established. Many mothers and doubtless a few of the younger midwives have probably had no experience whatever of the easy relaxed behaviour which can develop in breast feeding. The third and fourth day problems are rarely discussed in the antenatal period so that breast engorgement and other problems may come as a disagreeable surprise. If potential problems are considered in the antenatal period they may be overcome more readily. No two babies are alike and successful breast feeding will depend on the competence and temperament of the baby being sensitively matched to the competence, temperament and mammary capabilities of the mother. The milk ejection reflex takes some days or weeks to get established. A mother can be reassured of this very early on. Perhaps one of the more powerful and beneficial influences in a hospital ward is an experienced mother. Experimental studies of small groups demonstrate clearly the existence of 'informational social pressure' that is, in conditions where members of a group are unsure about what to do, an individual with relevant experience wields influence. A few breast feeding multiparae, well placed, could be a valuable resource to any midwife trying to encourage breast feeding.

Such mothers may also be able to demonstrate the fact that there is little direct relationship between breast size and milk supply. It is often claimed by the uninformed that the possession of small breasts rules out the possibility of breast feeding and pregnant women often express their anxiety about this. There are a few studies reported of mothers' attitudes to breast feeding but none concerning those of the people who are likely to attend her. The Association for the Improvement of the Maternity Services has found that mothers complain that one of the difficulties in establishing breast feeding is that they get inadequate or conflicting advice. This is not surprising as the most experienced midwives spend much of their time in administration and in initiating into ward policy and routine pupil midwives and obstetric nurses, some of whom stay for only a few weeks. Some units do the same with medical students and others grades of learners. The patients have, therefore, most contact with the least experienced staff who are not in a position to give suitable answers, but feel they must say something! More permanent members of the ward team are often part time which adds to the variety of advice and views, not all of which are up to date.

It seems often to be assumed that midwives themselves are all, by nature, not only in favour of babies being breast fed, but competent and at ease in discussing breast function and in giving practical aid and advice. Midwives, no less than their patients, are subject to the cultural influences which bear upon them. Personal feelings and professional tasks often need to be kept apart; experienced midwives and health visitors have probably evolved ways of doing this. But there may be a case for providing pupils with some facility for discussing conflicts and 'hang-ups' they may have about breasts and breast feeding.

People who are required to implement a policy to which they feel antagonistic, consciously or otherwise, are unlikely to be successful. Many mothers find breast feeding is much easier once they get home on their own territory. There are many aspects of hospital life which interfere with smooth relationships between members of a family and this is particularly so with a new member. During the later weeks of pregnancy some sort of 'nest building' activity is often apparent. Preparing a room, buying clothes and paraphernalia, delineating the territory, is part of the countdown. At the very moment of zero hour the mother is transferred to alien territory where, in the medicalised setting she takes on some aspects of the 'sick role'. The more thorough the medical attention she receives the more this role is enforced. Part of the sick role is to transfer responsibility. From the patients' point of view, at some times of the day, a ward can look like a railway station in the rush hour, with everyone seemingly bent upon his (or her) own business. Staff, trained, or learners of varying abilities, appear unexpectedly to either help with feeding or gather information. Doctors may do a rapid ward round between clinics or labour ward work. In

Figure 3.1. Baby grasping mother's fingers.

addition to ward staff there may be physiotherapists, laboratory staff, research workers and a variety of paramedical and social work personnel. In pursuit of their own tasks they inevitably interfere with individuals and can seriously disturb a mother whose baby is not yet feeding satisfactorily.

Even with early discharge home some of the most important experiences for mother and baby will have passed in hospital. At birth a normal full term baby has a number of reflexes present, which can be thought of as a rudimentary survival kit. The grasp, plantar, rooting and sucking reflex enable him in an emergency to hold on to mother and suck. These reflexes gradually give place to more discriminating learned behaviour. An older infant has learned what sort of objects bring a reward. There are, however, two kinds of sucking – nutritive and non-nutritive. Anyone who has watched small babies will have seen that they spend some time of each day 'mouthing' (i.e. moving their lips as if sucking). They also suck their fingers or a piece of blanket. Most young mammals engage in some non-nutritive sucking which is not necessarily related to hunger. Puppies who are given large feeds in a short time do a lot of non-nutritive sucking, as if they needed to perform a certain amount of activity. Breast fed babies do more non-nutritive sucking than bottle fed babies (Richards & Bernal 1972). Indeed the whole pattern of sucking, breathing and swallowing is different in bottle fed than in breast fed babies. Non-nutritive sucking is often looked upon as an index of alertness, and is often seen very soon after birth. Within a few minutes of being born some infants are vigorously sucking their fingers, yet it may be several hours before they are put to the breast. All newborn mammals make strenuous efforts to find the nipple. A healthy newborn baby held near to the breast will, by the functioning of the rooting reflex, find the nipple (though he is usually helped in this). From the moment he is born, learning about the environment takes place very rapidly. A baby who is put to the breast very shortly after birth possibly has this as his first positive learning experience. He will be learning about the shape and texture of the nipple, the smells, sounds and feelings (kinesthetic experience) that go with it. Babies will suck on a nipple or teat even when no food is forthcoming, while they remain unresponsive to food provided by a spoon. The experience of drawing the nipple to the back of the mouth seems to act as an initial reward in itself, and this is subsequently reinforced by the flow of milk. Two points follow: one is that the sucking is a good experience on its own. The fact that a small but nutritive amount of colostrum is the only food reward is not important. The other point is that the early learning about the smell, sounds, textures and so on, that are associated with feeding are very special: they may be the first learning that the baby does and they are very individual. Every mother has a particular smell, voice, way of holding her baby, and these characteristics are associated with feeding.

Figure 3.2. Baby breast feeding.

The gradual development of a positive response to the breast may easily be disturbed in the early days by someone else giving a complementary feed. The satisfaction of hunger is particularly likely to be associated with a lot of incidental learning so if we want the baby to learn how to breast feed it is better not to provide alternative learning situations for him. There is considerable evidence that mothers who are left on their own with their babies and encouraged to feed them on demand find it easier to establish breast feeding than in the cases where the care of the baby is divided in the first few days between nurse and mother.

On the mother's side her mothering role is likely to become stronger when she is left to work things out on her own. She may need some encouragement or even some suggestions as to how she might proceed in order to build her self-confidence. This is particularly important in a nervous patient who wishes to have a specified routine round which to organise her life, especially where family influence with regard to fixed interval feeding, has been strong. It is sometimes extremely difficult in a hospital setting to avoid undermining maternal confidence. The boundary between advising and interfering is usually somewhat fragile. There is the added difficulty in a hospital that the complexity of the apparatus, the efficiency and speed of the staff working under various constraints, the mechanisation, all manage to convey the impression that having and caring for a baby is a highly technical affair, only to be understood after years of experience or specialised training. During labour both mother and fetus are apt to become entangled in machinery incomprehensible to all laymen who are not electronically minded. After the baby is born it may need specialised attention. The likelihood is that it will be found whole and healthy, not by the inspecting eye of its own mother but by a highly trained midwife or paediatrician. An enquiry conducted by the National Childbirth Trust brought many complaints from mothers that after the birth they did not see their baby for some hours. The provision of a high level of specialised physical care can give the patient the impression that she is somewhat inadequate to care for her baby. There are probably few mothers, especially mothers of first babies, who do not feel they should take a subordinate role while in hospital. The hospital is alien territory – patients are there as guests and no guest feels it proper to be dominant in his host's home. A breast feeding relationship, however, is a primary and central one which is easily disrupted in hospital.

Because of the 'emergency' nature of a lot of hospital work and the demands of many and varied learners, hospital trained staff not infrequently have to develop a directive style of leadership. While suitable, indeed necessary, in many situations which arise in a hospital, it is not always helpful to a woman vacillating about her choice of feeding method. Attitudes to breasts and breast feeding are the products of life long subtle influences, and have strong emotional overtones. Emotional responses are rarely changed by direct factual information. In the Newcastle survey, already referred to, a third of the bottle-feeding mothers agreed it would be better for their baby to be breast fed. This knowledge did not however override their antagonistic feelings and although most mothers may want to do their best for their children, there is a point beyond which they will not go. There is quite a lot of evidence that if people are given unwelcome advice they are likely to strengthen their already existing attitudes. Their opinions may then move further away from that being advocated and also lead to a rejection of the source of the information as well, as the Newsons' study (1963) in Nottingham showed. There, some mothers rejected not only the advice but the health visitor herself together with the whole profession. This is a result entirely predictable where information, or instruction is given to an antagonistic audience. A more realistic attempt might be made if attitudes to breasts, breast feeding, having babies and rearing them could be brought out in an open-ended, non-directional discussion in a one-to-one or group setting. Cryptic leadership in such situations is a skilled task requiring not only the ability to listen and *hear,* but also to be able to tolerate and, if necessary, share the anxieties, aggressive feelings and other strong emotions that may be expressed.

As was mentioned in the Introduction, human breast milk is dilute and close in composition to the milk of other mammals who are continuous feeders. The study of a wide range of mammals shows that feeding patterns are intimately related to milk strength. Mammals with highly concentrated milk may feed their young as infrequently as once in 24 hours, while others with dilute milk carry and feed their offspring more or less continuously. The interval between feeds of different mammals has been found to be related not only to milk composition and growth rate of the young but also with the style of infant care (Ben Shaul 1962). Some mammals make nests where the young are left for long periods (e.g. rabbits), others, like most monkeys carry their offspring, who are able to cling on. The infants of most cloven footed mammals follow the mother from almost immediately after birth. The opportunities for feeding with these different kinds of infant care vary. It is now clear that in species which have concentrated milk there are long intervals between feeds, short feeds, and a high rate of sucking by the offspring. Conversely, dilute milk is associated with the reverse pattern. The details of this are less important than the general notion that a whole range of different factors are interdependent. A change in one of the factors may disrupt the smooth sequence of important activity.

Most of the artificial feeds available for babies are more concentrated than is human breast milk and this change may disrupt the natural pattern of sleeping, sucking and other activity of the infant. There are marked periodicities in normal infant feeding – the baby sucks quite vigorously for some seconds, rests, and then returns to sucking until another rest period. Breast and bottle fed babies have quite different patterns of sucking and resting. Not only do the babies behave differently but breast-feeding mothers, it has been found, interact with their babies between the bouts of sucking. It is then, during the rest period, that they may look, or smile, or talk to their babies. Bottle-feeding mothers are less phased in with their infants' activity in this way. A study in Cambridge in which mothers kept detailed diaries giving details of their daily activities, showed that successful breast-feeding mothers fed their babies more often. The mothers were found to be more responsive to their babies' needs and less constrained by preconceived ideas about what ought to be done. It was clear from that study that the four hourly feeds traditionally prescribed are too infrequent for some babies and that, particularly when the night feed is omitted, a rigid adherence to the clock may result in the infant being underfed. An essential feature of successful breast feeding is a relaxed relationship in which the mother can respond to her baby and learn from her observaticn of him. Babies, we now know can see much more than was previously believed. For them the mother is not just food but has a particular face to be looked at and explored, and a particular way of holding to be enjoyed and so on. Most mothers need an enhancement of their self-confidence, so that they can be satisfied with what they are doing in the vital steps in making a relationship with their baby. A good relationship cannot be built from a set of instructional rules. Observation and responsiveness are two essential ingredients and it is in these kinds of activity that mothers can be encouraged. Some may need rather more practical guidance than others. New babies can look very fragile and untouchable to someone with no previous experience of them. A simple word suggesting that a mother pick up her crying baby may still be necessary initially. Newly delivered mothers do not, generally speaking, have a reputation for high intelligence amongst the staff. To be uncertain about how to proceed can be guaranteed to make *anyone* seem foolish. Were she in her own home much of the patient's uncertainty would be resolved. The midwife has the vital task of helping a mother to resolve her uncertainties about the way she handles her baby, and as far as possible, to resolve many of the uncertainties intrinsic to the hospital situation. This may require suggestions and encouragement but not direct interference.

One of the disappointing features of the smaller four or six bedded wards is that the midwife cannot be so observant and her visits to the ward must usually seem more intentional. The older type of large ward, with its many disadvantages, at least provides an opportunity for unobtrusive observation or suggestion. Babies differ widely in all kinds of ways, the amount and timing of their sleep and wakefulness, their alertness, crying and speed with which they adapt to noise and other stimuli. We will discuss individual differences of babies in more detail in Chapter 5. The point here is that some of the characteristics of a baby, (for example the timing of his sleep) persist for months, sometimes years. As there are such wide variations from child to child a set of rules is likely to be inappropriate for some children. The responsiveness and flexibility required of a new mother is behaviour which most of us have been carefully trained *not* to do. The ideal of efficiency so pervasive in any advanced society, means going to school in time, catching trains, being at work – doing things by the clock. Innumerable psychological studies documenting differences between the sexes find men to be more task orientated, ambitious, assertive and women more person orientated, affiliative and submissive.

The changes in the role of women have been most apparent in the work setting. Almost all jobs are now in theory open to both men and women. Equality in the sex partnership and in the social role has also been largely achieved. Women with, or wanting babies, have been ill catered for by the various moves for the emancipation of women. The mother's role, if it is not to impose undue strain on some women, or indeed some families, needs to be more fully integrated into other roles that modern women occupy. As much of our economic and social lives is conducted outside our homes, child-rearing unavoidably adds a dimension to living which requires energy and planning if it is to be coordinated with an economic and social life. The traditional view that this makes a dual-role demand on women is giving place to the more egalitarian idea that it makes demands of both parents. Indeed, it is the shared parenting ideal which has often made bottle feeding so attractive. The accumulating evidence against early bottle-feeding, however, requires some modification in the provisions for the post-partum period. There are many obstacles in the way of a women who wants to nurture her totally dependent baby and hopes to maintain her economic and social life. The maternity allowance, payable for eleven weeks before the expected date of delivery and seven weeks afterwards is at present inflexibly administered. Many women are well able to continue to work for longer during their pregnancy, but the only way they can extend the post natal allowance is by falsifying their dates.

Figure 3.3. The sling is one way of conveying a baby without the mother needing to hold it. (Photograph by courtesy of Little Rock Ltd.)

Improvements in diagnostic techniques make this increasingly difficult! There is a strong case for not only making the allowance payable
more flexibly but also for extending it.

Neither women's fashions, nor the normal types of baby conveyance
are conducive to breast feeding. Some of the traditional women's
costumes of Europe and Asia were functional in this respect and it is
easy to see how breast feeding could take place without any public
exposure. Some current fashions are not helpful in this respect. The
grand perambulators which accompanied nannies on their course
through life have largely given place to lighter more adaptable prams
which can be put into cars and buses. There is a need for carry-on-the-
body type of conveyance which can support an infant without the
mother needing to hold it (Fig. 3.3).

Babies are associated with crying. In other parts of the world where
they are carried and suckled on demand a crying baby is hardly ever
heard. Were this the case here the resistance to admitting babies to
public places and to some working situations would be less. There are
some jobs which could be made compatible with the care of a small
baby. A teacher, midwife or health visitor with an accompanying
breast-fed baby would provide a very good practical example and
many hospitals now provide a crèche for their staff.

Many women feel extremely tired a few weeks post-partum. There
are two psychological situations which can be guaranteed to make the
most vigorous feel exhausted. One is boredom and the other is to be
indecisive over a personal conflict. The tiredness is usually explained
physiologically. It may equally be accounted for psychologically. The
smelling salts and vapours which were all accepted as part of the life for
the constrained, frustrated Victorian middle class women were in part
caused by the rigours of enclosing corsetry and in part by the utter
boredom and ennui of their respectable lives. Much less is heard of the
'vapours' since the *ennui* has been dispelled. *Ennui* is a mental
weariness stemming from lack of occupation or interest. It characterised the lives of Victorian women, and at one time its high incidence in
convents was of great concern to the church. Many of our assumptions
about women with very young babies are that they will stay at home,
foregoing many of their interests. What situation could be better
calculated to induce conflict and boredom? There is much that could
be done, and midwives and health visitors are in positions where they
can often initiate or influence decisions for improvements.

To summarise: the smooth integration of a new baby into the

Minds, Mothers and Midwives

family would be facilitated if the mother were able to continue in some of her previous activities, if not all. To an unnecessary extent the arrival of a new baby, especially the firstborn, often requires the mother to alter her life in a restrictive direction. Changes in women's social and work roles, have not yet accommodated the mothering requirements. There are many indications that these are being neglected or relegated to a secondary position with great cost to society.

REFERENCES

Bacon, C.J. & Wylie, J.M. (1976) *British Medical Journal,* **1** pp 308-9.
Ben Shaul, D.M. (1962) The composition of the milk of wild animals *International Zoological Year Book,* **4** pp 300-332.
de Sweit, M., Fayers, P., Cooper, L. (1977) *Lancet,* **1** pp 892.
Department of Health and Social Security (1974) *Present day practice in infant feeding.*
Eastham, E., Smith, D., Poole, D. & Neligan, G. (1976) *British Medical Journal,* **1** pp 305-307.
Frommer, E.A. (1973) *British Journal of Psychiatry,* **123** p 573.
Hubert, J. (1974) Belief and reality: social factors in pregnancy and childbirth. In *The Integration of the child into the Social World,* Ed. Richards, Martin P.M. London: Cambridge University Press.
Mackintosh, J.M. (1947) *British Medical Bulletin,* **5** pp 185-7.
Neville, J. (1976) *The Times* 7th April.
Newson, J. & Newson, E. (1963) *Infant care in an urban community.* London: Allen & Unwin.
Richards, M.P.M., & Bernal, J.F. (1972) An Observational study of mother-infant interaction. In *Ethological studies of child behaviour,* Ed. Blurton-Jones, N. London: Cambridge University Press.
Sosa, R., Kennell, J.H., Klaus, M. & Urrutia, J.J. (1976) The effect of early mother-infant contact on breast feeding, infection, and growth. In *Breast Feeding and the Mother,* Symposium 45. London: CIBA Foundation.

4

Neonatal abilities

Frederick Leboyer in his *Birth Without Violence* (1974) asks why nobody is concerned about the sufferings of the baby during birth. Considerable attempts have, after all, been made to relieve the pains of the mother for over a century. The answer he suggests is in the very commonly held view that new babies have no conscious awareness, that they can neither hear nor see and are incapable of intense feelings. William James who was appointed to the first ever Professorship in psychology in the 1890's described the world of the newborn as he imagined it, in the following terms: 'The baby assailed by eyes, ears, nose, skin and entrails at once feels that all is one great blooming buzzing confusion' (James, 1890). He seems to have thought that babies were capable of seeing and hearing, but that they were unable to organise the experience or to make any sense of it. This has been the view of most of the *experts* until recently. Some of the older textbooks on baby care and child development, go so far as to claim that a newborn infant is unable to see. A recent pamphlet published by the Health Education Council for the guidance of parents of young babies, says 'The only way a baby can recognise anything is through touch; he cannot yet understand the sounds that assault his ears, or the light that batters at his eyes'.

Many people who have a lot to do with new babies, have often wondered whether the experts are right. In the main we judge how a person experiences the world, by what he does or what he tells us about it. A new baby can do little of either, so it has been assumed that he experiences little. A similar idea sometimes prevails with a patient who seems to be unconscious, partly conscious, or has had a stroke. He can neither speak nor move; conversations take place over him, and discussions about him, which assume that he is deaf to the world, and without understanding or memory. Sadly this is often not true. He may be doubly distressed: first by what he hears, and secondly by his

49

inability to make this fact apparent to anyone. This is an experience incidentally, which occasionally occurs during a light anaesthetic, preceding the delivery of the baby in a caesarean section.

In trying to find out more precisely how newborn babies experience the world about them, a number of experimental techniques have been developed in the past few years, which have shown that despite his restricted motor capabilities, the human neonate has sensory and perceptual capabilities far beyond those accorded him. The techniques used in *asking* a newborn baby what he can perceive, what he prefers and remembers, depend on the measurement of motor activity (head turning, visual fixation, sucking etc.) and on physiological measures, for example, cardiac and respiratory changes, galvanic skin response and electro-encephalographic changes. A stimulus may evoke a particular activity or it may stop an activity. Some of these responses may be apparent to any careful observer. An example of this being that a particular sound may induce a baby to change his facial expression, or to disturb him from a restful state. If he is feeding, the same sound may cause him to stop sucking. These ways of responding are common enough to all of us. We turn with a *what's that?* expression to a new or unusual sound. If we happen to be doing something demanding our close attention, we stop to give full attention to the new stimulus. The orienting response and the cessation of other behaviour are both signs of being alert. When alert, both baby and adult are more perceptive. Alertness can be thought of as an increase in the general level of functioning. It is usually followed by organised attention to a particular feature of the environment, and the mobilisation of resources to deal with the stimulus. Recall, for example, a baby aroused for feeding. He becomes more active and bright, his activity then narrows down and becomes concentrated on the nipple and sucking, so that we can see the sequence: alerting, attention, action.

The techniques which have been used to assess perceptions and preferences of the newborn, depend on the careful observation and recording of motor activity and physiological changes. Using these techniques it is clear that neonates do perceive a great deal that was previously thought to be beyond their comprehension. Two other commonly held views of newborn babies may also have to be changed in the light of evidence now accumulating. The first is that activities of a new baby occur only in response to stimuli, either from outside or from internal organs. This concept may have to give place to that of an active little creature, who initiates things himself, and affects the behaviour of his parents, as well as responding to what happens to him. Secondly, a fairly commonly held idea, that babies are all alike and develop individuality as a result of their experiences will have to be modified to acknowledge a wide range of individual differences present from birth.

The picture which emerges of the newborn is that he has a considerable ability for perceiving his surroundings and for selecting some aspects as being more interesting and worthy of more prolonged attention. Secondly, he can initiate a sequence of behaviour as well as responding to outside stimuli. From the beginning of life he may show quite individual qualities of temperament, emotional traits and character which will contribute to his adult personality.

Long before he can explore his surroundings by direct touch, or by crawling and walking, he can explore with his eyes. Robert Fantz, a psychologist at Western Reserve University, U.S.A. has found that babies of a week old show a distinct preference for complex rather than simple visual patterns (Fantz, 1961). The baby, lying supine in the cot, had a series of pairs of patterns on the *ceiling* of the viewing box placed over the cot, at which he could look. A small peep hole in the ceiling and appropriate illumination enabled the experimenter to see the images of the pattern on the ceiling mirrored in the baby's eyes. When the baby looked directly at one of the patterns, the image over the pupil could be seen by the experimenter. The experimenter then recorded the amount of attention given to each pattern. The results show clearly that the more complex pattern receives more attention. For example, a red and white chequer board pattern has more than twice the attention of a plain red square of the same size alongside it. The pattern which has by far the most attention is that of a human face. The neonate looks most intently at an object which is at a distance of about 9 or 10 inches (23 to 25 centimetres) away from his eyes. The mammary glands being between the 2nd and 6th rib, ensures that when breast feeding the mother's face is just about that distance from the baby. She is positioned, therefore, for maximum learning if she looks at her baby in an *en face* position. In a recent study, however, it has been found that a larger number of breast feeders closed their eyes while feeding, and that when they do open their eyes, they do not necessarily look at the mother's face, but at the breast tissue (Infant Feeding Project, Wright, Crow and Fawcett, Edinburgh University). Some bottle feeding positions can extend beyond the optimal visual range of the infant. In a further development of this experimental technique, it has been shown how a newborn baby scans a pattern by visual exploration (Salapatek & Kessan, 1966). Pictures are taken which record the movements of the infant's eyes. When presented with a triangle the babies concentrate on the angles, so that the scanning pattern looks like this diagram (Fig. 4.1).

The triangles were above the head of
a one day old baby, in two positions.
Note focus on corners and edges (after Salapatek and Kessan 1966).

Figure 4.1. Visual scanning of triangles by the newborn.

The importance of this work is, that it shows clearly that a newborn infant does explore visually, and that some features of the environment do attract more attention than others. The *human face* pattern possibly has some important evolutionary significance. It is perhaps of elementary importance that the young should be able to distinguish adults of their own species without delay. These experiments, however, help us to describe what the infant does, rather than why he does it. He explores visually; particular objects attract his attention; he can focus on them and scan them.

A much earlier study (Chase 1937) showed clearly that babies of 15 days old could discriminate among a range of colours. In studying colour discrimination, however, it is not clear whether the infant is responding to brightness or to hue. Yellow, for example, is brighter than blue and is also a different hue. Hue, which is the dimension of blueness or yellowness, depends on the wavelength of the light, and brightness on the amplitude of the wave. It is not clear either, whether babies of under 16 days can distinguish between one colour and another.

Figure 4.2. Baby looking over mother's shoulder becomes visually alert.

In view of the neonates locomotor helplessness, vision is a most important avenue for learning, and getting to know the world he lives in. It will be a common enough experience to midwives that when babies are picked up to be consoled, they are often held so that they are looking over the adult's shoulder (Fig. 4.2). When this happens many babies stop crying and become visually alert. Opening the eyes in this way does not happen when the infant is simply handled, nor when he is placed in an upright position only (Korna & Grobstein 1966). The opportunity to look round and to experience the world may play a crucial role in early development. A mother who holds her baby in an upright viewing position is inadvertently also providing him with new experiences, and an opportunity for learning. Much attention has been paid to the influence of maternal care and handling on the development of emotional security. It is also proper to consider the effect of maternal behaviour on the intellectual development of the infant. When a mother picks up her baby, she is aiding both the development of emotional security by providing warmth and assurance and at the same time, widening his perceptual field, and thereby encouraging his intellectual development.

Mention has already been made of the preference neonates show for a black and white model of a human face, over a patterned stimulus. Genevieve Carpenter (Carpenter *et al*, 1970) has found that from the

Figure 4.3. Mother and baby inspecting each other at the earliest opportunity.

age of one week, a baby responds differently to his mother's face and that of a model. It can be inferred therefore, that some recognition of the mother's face is possible. Recognition is only possible if something is remembered. The idea that a baby can remember anything at a week old, would probably not be conceded by most people working with mothers and young babies on the basis of normal observations, and shows both the value and the need for, special techniques which have been developed in the last decade, for observing and recording infant behaviour.

If babies are able to both perceive and learn, at such an early age, fresh questions arise about their care in hospital, in the immediate post-natal period. We have already seen in the Chapter on Feeding (see Ch. 3) that breast feeding is prolonged when mother and baby are in close proximity for about an hour after birth. It has been assumed that the mother is favourably influenced by the opportunity to inspect and handle her new baby without interference. We now have to consider the effect on the baby of a prolonged opportunity of examining his mother's face. Mother and baby's inspection of each other provides the opportunity for each to learn about the other (Fig. 4.3). In adulthood mutual gaze has always been recognised as an important means of communication. The eyes have been referred to romantically as the *windows of the soul* and prolonged eye to eye contact is traditionally associated with falling in love. The mother may never again have the freedom to spend such long periods of time looking at, cuddling, and nursing her baby. The ten days or so in hospital where the mother is free from domestic concerns, and other children, could be of immense value. Mothers often become quite excited if their babies look at them. The care and attention the mother gives her baby is made much more rewarding by an attentive infant. The potential opportunities for mother and baby rarely materialise in hospital, however, as there are apparently endless practical reasons for interfering between mother and baby and disrupting their relationship.

Greenman (1963) has found that 95 per cent of normal infants, normally delivered, can follow an object visually. He used a four inch (10 cms) red ring at approximately 10 inches (25 cms) from the face, when the baby was supine, within 96 hours of birth. Where central nervous system damage has occurred the moro reflex, grasping, automatic walking are usually normal, but it is the visual following which is lacking. This may clearly affect the social relations between mother and baby. A moderate degree of photophobia during the first few days of life has been noted. The study of the visual behaviour of newborn babies usually has to be done in a subdued light, or the infant will not open his eyes at all. It has also been found that babies not only look round in the dark, but they open their eyes and actively *search* by scanning when the light is put off (Haith 1972).

Reduced illumination is one of the features of Leboyer's method of delivery, and favourable comment has been made about the apparent alertness of the infants, which may, of course, be due to other features of his method. Whether an infant's eyes are open or shut is likely to affect both his social relations and his learning. In normally sighted human beings the very great majority of information about the world comes through the eyes. There are important things to be learned in the first few days of life, and this is the time when social communication between mother and baby begins.

The ability of the very young of several species of animal to perceive depth, has been established by the use of a test apparatus known as a visual cliff (Gibson and Walk 1960). This consists of a patterned chequered floor with a raised platform of the same pattern. The platform is covered with a glass plate which extends right over the lower section. Young animals placed on the platform side will explore, but always stop at the platform edge. The *drop* is visible, although the glass plate provides a continuous firm flat floor. Young children who

Figure 4.4. Child stops at the visual cliff edge of a patterned platform. (after Gibson and Walk).

can crawl have been tested with the visual cliff, and they too stop at the cliff edge (Fig. 4.4).

A crawling baby has several months in which to learn about depth, however, and this tells us nothing about the neonate. By comparing recordings of the heart rate of very much younger babies placed over the shallow and the deep side it is plain that they can discriminate the difference. Neonates have not been tested in this way yet, but what does emerge is that babies of eight weeks old show no distress outwardly but a marked response of their autonomic system. Older children show marked distress. It has been suggested (Campos, Langer & Krow 1970) that there is a developmental delay between the ability to distinguish a stimulus, and the ability to communicate the fact by an emotional response. The limitations of their emotional expression may not reflect limitations of their experience. In other words, it is unjustified to assume that because a new baby fails to smile, he is not experiencing pleasure, or because he does not show boredom he is not needing something interesting to look at or listen to. The experience which is accumulating in the early days and weeks will be of the greatest importance at a later stage. With increasing physical maturation he will be able to act on information acquired earlier.

Jean Liedloff (1975) mentions an incident in which an American child who was prevented by fences and locked gates from exploring in the family swimming pool area. When it finally got through the barricade it fell in the pool and was drowned. She contrasts the behaviour of parents and child in this setting with that of the Yequana, a primitive jungle tribe of Venezuela, with whom she had spent two and a half years. Children there play unsupervised around a pit and never get into difficulties. It is possible that the Yequana children are able to develop their appreciation of the depth on the basis of an innate fear. The American child was restrained and may have been prevented from acquiring an important experience which he needed for his own protection when exploring. Young children rarely fall down the stairs when they are crawling: they can perceive a change in depth and stop at the top of the stairs. Falling down the stairs is more common when the child begins walking upright, and is a bit clumsy or unsteady.

Various methods are employed to assess hearing in the newborn. These include the observation of movements, changes in respiration, in electroencephalograph, of skin resistance, cardiac changes and the inhibition of sucking. From a wide range of studies it is clear that normal neonates can appreciate differences in pitch, rhythm, and loudness. The heart rate of babies between one and nine days old has been found to increase in a regular way with an increase in the loudness of a tone (Bartoshuk 1974).

Almost any healthy newborn baby will be aroused by a distinctive sound. The Brazelton Neonatal Behavioural Assessment Score utilizes three kinds of sound to assess not only the infant's ability to hear, but also his ability to learn from what he is hearing. A rattle, a bell and a human voice are used. We have already explained in Chapter 1 how babies differ in their ability to learn about sounds. Some become accustomed to the sound, and show that they can ignore it by not responding (response decrement) quite quickly, and others take much longer. Selecting appropriate signals for attention is an essential part of survival. If too many stimuli attract attention, the individual will be overwhelmed. If too few are used, he may miss an essential one. Habituation is an important process which from birth, and probably before, helps us ignore the repetitive, predictable signals, thereby allowing more time and energy for the new and unusual features of the surrounding world. The normal healthy baby is aroused by the rattle, the bell and the human voice. He may show a general startling, or localised response – such as tight blinking, or respiratory changes. When the baby has settled, the stimulus is presented again, and then after a rest period it is repeated and so on. The fact that, despite individual variations, all babies eventually *shut down* and ignore the stimulus, indicates that they are learning that it is a signal which is irrelevant. Babies can sleep soundly in a place where there is a lot of noise, providing it is a noise to which they have become accustomed. It is the smooth monotony of many lullabies which makes them effective. The unexpected sound produces arousal and wakefulness.

Full term normal healthy newborn infants do vary in maturity. Girls, on average, have a more mature nervous system than boys, and it is probably only the more mature infants who are able, in the first two or three weeks, to integrate what they hear with what they see. The orienting reflex – turning to look at a source of sound or movement – so obvious in older children and adults, is not consistently apparent until several months after birth. It has been called the *what's that?* response. A small proportion of babies will turn to look at the source of the human voice. This is very exciting for a mother if her baby turns to look at her when she calls him by name.

Odours are another set of stimuli to which newborn babies will respond. In one study which tested babies on the first, second, third and fourth days of life, for their responsiveness to different concentrations of asafoetida (a gum resin of various oriental plants of the carrot family), it was found that the sensitivity of the babies increased each day, and they were able to respond to smaller concentrations. It is not clear from this whether this improvement in sensitivity is due to maturation or to learning. This increase in sensitivity may seem to contradict our previous comments about response decrement. Response decrement occurs when a single persistent unvarying kind of stimulus is presented. Its monotony and essential lack of significance to the infant, causes the decrease in response. An important feature in the development of heightened sensitivity, is that different stimuli are present, in this case different concentrations, so that the infant has the opportunity of detecting and responding to small changes in his surroundings.

A story is told of Ludwig Koch, a naturalist famous for his detailed knowledge of birds and bird song. He was making a recording of an unusual bird song in Regent's Park. When he played his recording back, all that could be heard was the traffic in the Marylebone Road. He had become habituated to the traffic – it was monotonous and of no significance to him – so much so, that he did not recognise its presence. The bird song to which he had become highly sensitised by years of attentive listening to small changes, was all he could hear. The tape recorder had no such selective perception.

A further indication that the infant receives information and learns about his surroundings through his sense of smell, comes from the finding that at two weeks old a baby is more likely to turn his head in the direction of his mother's breast pad than that of any other lactating mother (McFarlane 1975). The mother's smell is one of many stimuli which go to make up the total experience for the baby, of his mother. There are, as has already been mentioned, innumerable interferences between the two while they are in hospital. If smell is important, what effects have the various therapeutic and cosmetic creams and potions which are applied to the nipples and body generally? We do not know. Alterations in the mother's odour may affect the baby's interest in breast feeding as well as his learning about her. Cleaning the areola and the nipple and then applying lanoline is an interference with a natural process which is often avoidable. The sense of smell is more important to many adult animals than it is to adult humans. The area of the brain which is associated with olfaction is in the paleocortex, that part of the cortex which appeared relatively early in the evolution of the brain. The development of the neo-cortex is generally considered to be associated with evolutionary advance in psychomotor and language skills. It is likely that young babies, therefore, depend more than adults on the relatively primitive sense of smell. The possible existence and likely action of human pheromones has been debated in the past few years. A pheromone is an odour which functions as part of a signalling system, and can both arouse and guide behaviour. Pheromonal substances may be released from apocrine glands, axillary secretion or smegma. It has been suggested that pheromones may be important in sexual and social relationships, as well as in infant-parent and child-parent relations, (Comfort 1971). It is often found that a particular odour evokes a long past memory with great clarity. The smell of a house in which some childhood holiday was spent, or the scent of a particular person's clothing may set in motion a whole sequence of recollections.

Little research has been done of infants' taste. It is difficult to avoid confusion of taste with smell. Babies do, however, seem to have an established hierarchy of preferences in the order sweet, salt, sour, bitter.

Babies also experience the world about them through touch, handling, being cuddled, stroked or rocked. Left to themselves

Figure 4.5a Mother examining newly born baby by feeling, stroking and cuddling.
& 4.5b

mothers will often examine their just born baby by feeling its limbs, stroking it and then cuddling it (Fig. 4.5a&b).

When Harlow separated rhesus monkey babies from their mothers they spent far more time with the soft towelling model in spite of the fact that their food supply was dispensed by the wire one (See Ch. 1). The towelling attracted and satisfied the babies, but when they reached adulthood they had great difficulties in their relationships with other adult rhesus monkeys, and also in caring for their own babies. The towelling mother surrogates did not, of course, handle and carry them in the way a living mother would have done, and they, therefore, had no opportunity to learn important things about their own species.

Mothers and babies who have had the opportunity to experience skin contact for an hour or so after birth have measurable differences in their behaviour, as compared with those who follow the normal hospital routine in which the mother is attended to while the baby is cleaned and dressed elsewhere, put in his cot and sent to the nursery. These studies have already been referred to in Chapter 3 as the extended contact mothers are more likely to persist with breast feeding. They also pay more attention to their babies, and the babies are more advanced by the time they are two years of age.

Many paintings of mothers and babies show the baby being held on the left side of the mother's body. Mother Rhesus monkeys are also more likely to carry their newborn infants on the left. Lee Salk, an American psychologist, has been able to demonstrate in a series of experiments, that in the normal mother and baby relationship, the baby is held on the left side. This applies equally to both left and right handed mothers. He thought this might be because the infant was more peaceful on the left side close to the mother's heart. For nine months he has been developing in close proximity to the aorta. Perhaps, during intrauterine life the infant has learned an association between the rhythmical heart beat, and the protected tension free state. Salk compared two groups of newborn infants. One group of 102 babies were placed in a nursery immediately after birth, and were kept there for four days, except for normal feeding by their mothers every four hours. A recording of the sound of an adult heart beat, 72 beats per minute at 85 decibels played continuously day and night. Another group of 112 infants were kept in a quiet nursery. The two groups were compared for weight change and amount of crying. Those infants in the heart beat nursery had a median weight gain of 40 grams, and the control group a median loss of 20 grams. There were no significant differences in food intake between the two. There was crying for 38 per cent of the time in the heart beat nursery and for 60 per cent of the time in the control group (Fig. 4.6). These results suggest that newborn infants are soothed by the sound of the normal adult heart beat. A recording firm has recently made a record of heart beat sounds which is marketed as a baby soother.

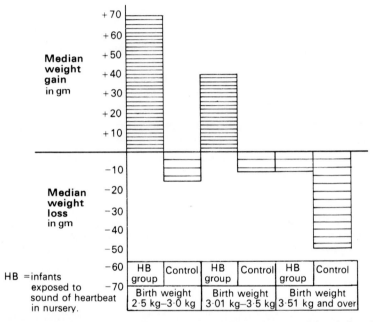

Figure 4.6. Diagram to show effect of recorded adult heart beat on weight gain from 1 to 4 days after birth where amount of feeds were similar (after Salk).

We have come to understand more about the world of the neonate by observing one aspect of his behaviour at a time, and by presenting him with one isolated stimulus at a time. We can appreciate some of his preferences and predelections. Babies, however, normally have to deal with a whole mother – face, colour, sound, smell, heartbeat, nipple, warmth, movement, arms, body – all at once. Mother and baby need opportunities for learning about each other as whole human beings, of learning to understand and respond to each other. If they can be assured of these opportunities in the two weeks after birth, they can go home together with more than a satisfactory weight gain for the baby, and an involuted uterus and well healed perineum for the mother. They are likely to have a good foundation for a happy and understanding relationship, which will reduce the risk of acute anxiety which a young mother all too often experiences.

REFERENCES

Bartoshuk, A.K. (1964) Intensity of Sound. *Psychonomic Science,* **1** pp 151-2.

Campos, J.J., Langer, A., Krow, A. (1970) *Science,* **170** pp 196-7.

Carpenter, G.C., Tecce, J.J., Stechler, G., Friedman, S. (1970) Differential visual behaviour to human and humanoid faces in early infancy. *Merrill Palmer Quarterly,* **16** pp 91-108.

Chase, W.P. (1937) Colour vision in infants. *Journal of Experimental Psychology,* **20** pp 203-222.

Comfort, A. (1971) Likelihood of human pheromones. *Nature,* **230** pp 432-433.

Fantz, R. (1961) *Scientific American,* **204** pp 66-72.

Gibson, E.J. & Walk, R.D. (1960) The visual cliff. *Scientific American,* **202** iv pp 64-71.

Greenman, G.W. (1963) In *Modern perspectives in child development.* Ed. Solnit, A.J. & Provence, S.A. New York: Hallmark.

Haith, M.H. (1972) Visual scanning in infants. In *The Competent Infant,* Ed. Stone, L.J., Smith, H.T., & Murphy, L.B. pp 320-323. London: Tavistock Publications.

James, W. (1890) *Principles of Psychology,* p 488. New York: Holt.

Korna, A.F. & Grobstein, R. (1966) Visual alertness as related to soothing in neonates. *Child Development,* **37** No. 4 pp 867-876.

Leboyer, F. (1974) *Birth without violence.* London: Wildwood House Ltd.

Leidloff, J. (1975) *The Continuum concept.* London: Duckworth.

McFarlane, J.A. (1975) Olfaction in the development of social preferences in the human neonate. In *Parent-Infant Interaction.* Symposium No. 33, London: CIBA Foundation.

Salapatek, P.H. & Kessan, W. (1966) Visual scanning of geometric figures in the human newborn. *Journal of Experimental Child Psychology,* **3** pp 155-167.

Salk, L. (1973) The role of the heartbeat in the relationship between mother and infant. *Scientific American,* **228** pp 24-28.

Wright, P., Crow, R. & Fawcett, G. Personal communication.

5

Development

A midwife's primary concern is the health, comfort and happiness of the mother and baby. Although it is the pregnancy, labour and puerperium which are within the midwife's immediate purview, it is the long term effects of events during that period that are of wider concern.

Babies in some respects are all alike – any human infant is distinguishable from any other new born mammal. There are also ways in which a baby is like some other babies. A boy, for example, has some qualities and characteristics in common with all other boys, and these characteristics distinguish him from all girls. There are innumerable criteria for putting people into sub categories. There are also ways in which each baby is a unique individual – his totality of qualities and characteristics that make up his quite distinctive identity.

At conception half the chromosomes from each parent join together to form the first cell, or zygote, of the new individual. The 50 per cent of parental chromosomes which go to the formation of the ovum or the spermatozoon, seems to be largely a matter of chance. From, possibly millions of spermatozoa, only one will fertilise the ovum; which one, is again a matter of chance. Before the zygote has begun to develop the assortment of genetic material is such as to make predictions about the offspring from a knowledge of the parents, something of a gamble. As soon as the ovum has been fertilised, it begins to develop in an environment. The importance of this prenatal environment is discussed in the chapter about antenatal events.

Almost every individual varies in his genetic endowment and his experiences. If two factors vary at the same time, it is impossible to find out which one is responsible for an observed difference. Is a child good at mathematics because he has an inborn aptitude (heredity) or because he has had special training e.g. a particularly good teacher (environment), or because his inherited predisposition and experience have interacted in an advantageous way? In the case of one individual, it is often impossible to say how far a particular characteristic is derived from environmental factors and how far from heredity. The nature–nurture issue has been the subject of endless debate. 'What's born in the blood comes out in the bone' is a saying supporting the *nature* side of the argument while 'as the twig is bent so the tree grows' supports the *nurture* side. This is an issue of great importance to everyone who has anything to do with child care. If development depends primarily on *nature* then variations in *nurture* will have relatively little impact. Much of the endeavour in the biological and behavioural sciences, have been directed to finding out what changes in *nurture*, do, or can affect development. Improvements in obstetrics, in baby feeding, in special provisions for small, preterm or sick babies have all helped to reduce the infant mortality rate, and to reduce morbidity.

What do we know of the factors which can affect long term happiness, achievement, learning ability, concentration, ability to think and reflect, self assurance, anxiety, which are also of such importance in good physical and mental health? These psychological features, and many more, are derived from either *nature*, or *nurture*, or are a product of some interaction between the two.

Psychologists have tried to tease out some answers to these questions by a number of different methods. Experiments with animals can sometimes provide important clues and ideas, but it is wrong to extrapolate from animal studies to human beings as if they are much alike. The response of human beings to any experience is complicated by their use of language and their complex social structure.

The question of the effect of fetal environment on development is dealt with in detail in the chapter on antenatal events. The way in which the fetus develops may have long term consequences for the development of the child. The uterine environment may give rise to subtle changes which though causing no macroscopic abnormality, may somehow affect the developing neural tissues of the fetus which govern behaviour in later life. De Licardie and Cravioto (1974) have shown how poor diet affects long term development and intellectual achievement. The National Child Development Study has found that children of mothers who smoked during the pregnancy have a depressed reading age at seven years (Davie, Butler & Goldstein 1972). Hypoxia may affect brain tissue extensively, producing long term problems such as subnormality, clumsiness, speech defects, poor motor coordination and behaviour problems. Chronic hypoxia may be caused by placental insufficiency of unknown aetiology, or that associated with hypertension, renal disease, and other adverse factors. The long term effects for the child, the family and the community, of these very early events are of great consequence. One of the trials of life is that the poor conditions during pregnancy which contribute towards difficulties in the offspring, are more common in lower working class families, who are least able to contend with the additional strain imposed by a less-than-whole child.

Identical (uniovular) twins have been studied quite extensively. They provide a natural occurring situation in which inherited factors are constant, as they have developed from a single zygote. Identical twins, however, normally grow up in the same family, and experience very similar environments. Occasionally identical twins are separated. Such separated uniovular twins have been the basis of a few important studies of development, as they provide conditions in which one of the variables in the important nature–nurture equation is the same. Observed differences between the twins may reasonably be attributed to differences in their background, upbringing, experiences – in short, to their *nurture*.

A further method is to assess the effects of either enhancing or depriving a group of children of an experience, and comparing them with another group who have not been so treated. The intentional deprivation of a group of children for scientific purposes would, needless to say, be unethical, but there are plenty of spontaneously occurring deprivations the effects of which can be, and have been, assessed. Intentional enhancement is often severely frowned upon as well, as it is considered improper to provide a supposed advantage to one but not to all.

Several of the sources of information already referred to in this book are based on ethological studies. Ethology first emerged in the 1950s, as the study of animal behaviour, and was concerned with the detailed observation of behaviour which occurred naturally in the normal habitat. The first ethologists were critical of the *experimental laboratory* approach to behaviour, which required the animal (or human) to perform a sequence of behaviour which was often quite foreign to him under artifical conditions. Ethological studies of child behaviour are those in which careful observations are made of the child, or mother and child in the course of their normal daily life, for example – what does a mother do when her baby cries? The answer to that question probably has an important bearing on how the infant develops socially and emotionally. By noting carefully, sometimes with the aid of a videotaped recording, how a number of mothers and babies behave with each other, it has been possible to come to some general conclusions about particular aspects of child development. In this chapter we shall refer to information culled from the study of sub-human mammals, twins, groups of children who have been enhanced or deprived of particular experiences, and from ethological studies.

A number of apocryphal stories about feral children reared by animals exist. There are few properly documented accounts of the development of children grossly deprived of any sort of human contact. Those which do exist make it plain that many of the qualities and traits we regard as characteristically human are learned; the upright posture, speech, the communicative gesture and facial expressions need either example or precept to emerge. In the absence of facilitative experience the inborn capacity for a whole range of behaviour remains dormant.

Many years ago Jean-Marc-Gaspard Itard published an account of his attempts to humanise a boy who had lived wild in the woods around Paris. *The Wild Boy of Aveyron* is one of the earliest studies of the effect of environment on growth and behaviour.

Fortunately such bizarre experiences are extremely rare. Children brought up in institutions usually have a background distinctively different from that of children in families, and have been the subject of concern for almost a century. Published figures in Europe and America showed that in the first two decades of this century the mortality rate of infants reared in institutions was extremely high – between 30 per cent and 100 per cent. By the 1940s this high mortality rate had been reduced, and was in line with that of the general population. With the survival of institutionalised children a new problem emerged. '. . . Institutionalised children, practically without exception developed subsequent psychiatric disturbances and became a social, delinquent, feeble minded, psychotic and problem children.' In this country the recommendations of the Curtis Report on the care of children deprived of a normal home life (Report on the Care of Children Committee 1947) and Bowlby's report for the World Health Organisation drew attention to some of the important factors which seemed to the authors to contribute to intellectual, emotional and social difficulties of infants and children in orphanages and foundling homes. Institutional life is characterised by impersonal relationships, regimentation, an emphasis on order, cleanliness and discipline. Children reared in families grow up by and large, without the problems which beset a considerable proportion of those reared in institutions. This broad comparison of two large groups of children led to specific conclusions and recommendations. The Curtis Report recommended fostering for young children, where possible. Where it was not possible, a more homely atmosphere, with smaller groups of children, and an identifiable house parent was advocated. Bowlby identified the source of the problem for children in institutions as that of being deprived of their mother. He claimed that a warm, continuous, and intimate relationship with his mother, or a mother surrogate, was essential for the child's good mental health. Bowlby has been the single most important influence on thinking about the child's mental development in this country. Many of the cruder effects on children of going to hospital and into children's homes, can now be ameliorated, if opportunities are provided for visiting, and for the maintenance or cultivation of a close personal affectionate relationship. It is a measure of the success of Bowlby's proselytising that everyone now seems to recognise, that as well as food and warmth, an infant needs loving care and attention. For comparison look at some of the child care manuals published before the 1940s. Their emphasis was mainly on feeding, cleanliness, and discipline and order. Affectionate attention by parents was seldom mentioned and sometimes regarded as a sign of moral turpitude.

The importance of a loving relationship between mother and child leads, according to Bowlby, to *bonding* between the two. In later writing, Bowlby (1969) has used the term *attachment* in place of *bonding*. The attachment to an adult of the species, is an important feature in the development of the young, of a large number of birds and animals, as has been discovered by the ethologists. A lot of species-appropriate behaviour can be learned from the adult to whom the infant becomes attached. In quite normal families infants may develop multiple attachments, or they may be devoted to an adult other than their mother. Some youngsters become specially devoted to an older sibling, their father, or a grandmother for example. What does seem to be of great importance is that the person or persons with whom a particular affection is developed, should maintain the relationship. One of the damaging experiences in institutional homes derived, and still does, from the fact that staff so frequently change and special attachments have little opportunity to flourish.

The first two years of life is a period during which affectionate attachment for one, or a few people, develops with ease if the infant is lovingly cared for and attended. Some psychologists disapprove of the term *attachment* as it suggests an almost mechanical relationship – perhaps like being tied together with a rope. Any mechanical analogy of this sort may mask the important fact that the relationship is essentially a social one, which depends on subtle signals and learning for its development. How readily a satisfactory and rewarding relationship can develop later on, if it fails to do so in the early years, is still a matter of debate. What does seem reasonably clear is that the first experiences of other people who are important in the infant's world, form something of a prototype for subsequent encounters. If the initial experiences are uncomfortable and unrewarding those which follow are not embarked upon with trust and social ease.

Children learn from their parents and caretakers, but so do parents learn from their children. A mother with a new baby often looks and feels ill at ease because she has no experience in interpreting what the needs of the child are, and does not know how to handle him. She learns a great deal by noticing what he likes and dislikes. The process whereby the parents and siblings become attached to the new member of the family, are perhaps as important as the process by which he becomes attached to them.

Affection, security, warmth, continuity, intimacy, describe positive emotional qualities of a relationship. The child who experiences them is likely to develop similar qualities. As a child grows older he will want to explore, to try out his own abilities, and to find things out for himself. Finding out about his surroundings – what they are made of, how they work, and so on, form an important part of the child's intellectual development. Children who are emotionally insecure are easily frightened. Easily frightened children don't explore. Children who don't explore don't learn. So having a good relationship which generates a feeling of security is important, not only for emotional well-being, but has an important bearing on the way a child builds up a store of knowledge about the world.

There are a number of features which affect the emotional stability, in addition to the sort of relationship the infant enjoys in early life. There is good evidence that emotionality is in part innate (Shields 1962). One long term study which followed children from birth to ten shows how persistent emotional characteristics assessed at birth are (Thomas, Chess and Birch 1970). The tendency to be excitable or placid, shows at or soon after birth. Babies, like adults, vary in the speed at which they habituate. This variation is made use of in the Brazelton Assessment Scale of Neonatal Abilities (see Ch. 4).

A young baby explores with his eyes, later with his hands, and as soon as he can crawl or walk, he becomes vigorously active in his search for novelty. An attempt has been made to account for changes in interest and attention, by the discrepancy hypothesis which runs thus:

> When faced with a new stimulus we match it against information we already have stored in our memory. If the new stimulus exactly fits a stored image or memory, little interest is aroused – it is entirely predicatable and boring. If it is very different from the stored memory, it is too novel, alarming, and arouses fear, and thus inhibits curiosity. It is the stimulus with some recognisable, and also some novel features, which maximises curiosity and exploration.

These three separate factors, innate emotionality, early experience, and the degree of novelty in a situation will affect the interest, and attention, a child can devote to his surroundings, and hence the amount he can learn. The child who fidgets, is unable to concentrate and is easily distractable, usually has a difficult time at school, and compares unfavourably with the youngster who is able to approach a new problem with interested concentration. An important dimension which emerges in children of school age is that of reflectivity and impulsiveness (Kagan & Freeman, 1963).

The reflective child when faced with a problem thinks before acting or speaking, whereas the impulsive one tries an immediate solution to the problem, fails, is upset by his failure, and makes further impulsive attempts becoming more and more frustrated.

It is by no means far fetched to suggest that the midwife may have an important part to play in the long term emotional and intellectual development of the normal babies for whom she cares. (The small, ill or handicapped infants are discussed in Chapter 6).) Variations in innate emotionality cannot be altered. Some babies will be by nature more restless, will cry more and be more difficult to settle than others. These babies will need more skilled handling and patience, and their mothers, especially the inexperienced, may not be very good initially, at providing this. A midwife may be able to give an example to an inexperienced mother and also to help her to keep calm and patient. Placid babies usually make for placid mothers and the converse is also true. Any midwife who can help to introduce stability and calm into the relationship, may make a valuable contribution to the baby's long term development.

As has been mentioned elsewhere, Richards (1975) has shown that the pattern of crying is a relatively persistent characteristic of a baby, and it is important, therefore, that the mother is not made to feel she is mishandling him. It may be necessary to acknowledge the fact that the baby is *not* going to turn into a placid peaceful child, and to help the mother adjust *her* life to accord with the infant's needs. The mother of a fidgeting or fretful baby, is likely to be grateful for months ahead for any help, example, or encouragement which leads to her more successful adjustment to the infant.

Ideally everyone has an optimal degree of arousal at which learning is maximised. Insufficient arousal induces apathy and a lack of awareness; excessive arousal means too much anxiety and emotion, which can be disruptive. Learning requires not only a suitable state in the learner, but something *out there* to be learned. A dull environment is likely to make a dull child. Young animals who have been reared with things to play with, turn out to be more intelligent than similar litter mates who have only been able to *look* at the play objects, and they in turn are brighter than animals who have had neither opportunity to *feel* or *see* a variety of objects (Forgus 1966).

It is now a truism that children who have the benefit of a more stimulating environment, generally develop into brighter people. A stimulating environment means one which provides a wide range of experiences with things to look at, hear, touch, and with opportunities for exploration, manipulation, and play with things and people. The abilities of the newborn are considerably more advanced than many people have supposed. In order to develop an ability it needs opportunity for exercise. It follows, therefore, that if an infant can distinguish shapes, colour and pattern, an opportunity for development is being missed if he cannot visually explore such things. Fantz (1966) has found that he can distinguish babies who have been brought up in an institution from those who are reared at home, by their visual responses at two months old. Babies cared for by their own mothers are probably exposed to a richer visual environment as they are picked up more often and have the chance to look round. The long term consequences of this, of course, are not known, but the first two months of life is only lived through once. It is from this kind of detailed study, that the precise meaning of institutional deprivation begins to be clarified.

Another area of experience, which is of powerful importance in intellectual development, is in language learning. We need words to describe and communicate our experiences, but they also help us to make perceptual discriminations. We probably all have some practical experience of this fact if we recall the process of some new learning. In midwifery for example, we used to learn about the premature baby. The concept of prematurity we now know confuses two different problems namely, pre-term birth and slow intra-uterine growth. Both result in a low birth weight baby. The more discriminating perception of pre-term-ness and small-for-dates-ness required new words as labels. These words, in turn, help a student to perceive differences between the two kinds of baby. The distinction between the two has led to improvements in treatment and prognosis. The perception, and the word-label which denotes it are closely associated together.

Much education depends on a refinement of perception. In advanced society, education at all levels proceeds mainly by teaching – through the spoken or written word. This is in contrast to primitive societies where education procedes by showing, and the learner is immediately involved in the task situation of, say hunting or cooking. This means that achievements and satisfactions, in an advanced society, not only within the educational system, but in life generally, are very likely to be associated with good linguistic and verbal abilities. Children do not normally speak their first words until they are about a year old. As anyone who has learned a foreign language can readily appreciate, however, there is a distinction between passive and active language. Passive language refers to the considerable understanding which usually precedes the ability to speak. Institutional children, it has been found, have fewer words in their repertoire than have home reared children. Well before any question of words or language arises, there are measurable differences in, not only the number of sounds which the two groups of children make, but the number of times they make them (Irwin 1949).

From within a few days or weeks of birth, vocalisation is encouraged by the mother who talks to or answers her child when he makes a sound, which includes crying. The infant who burbles and cries and receives no *sound* in reply, is less likely to continue sound making, and also less able to learn different kinds of sound. Innumerable follow-up studies of infants both normal and disadvantaged at birth, testify to the fact that the socio-economic position of the families in which they are reared, is of overwhelming importance to their long term development. In what way does the home of the higher social class child differ from that of the lower class child? To generalise from a number of studies it is clear that middle class mothers engage in much more verbal interaction, (Levine, Fishman and Kagan 1967; Tulkin and Kagan 1972) and working class parents provide more physical stimulation for their infants (Moss, Robson and Pedersen 1969). No substantial difference between the classes has been established so far as affective (emotional) behaviour is concerned (Bayley and Shaefer 1960; Kagan and Freeman 1963). Middle class parents seem to provide a greater variety of stimulation, and markedly more verbal variety. It is important to recognise that these variations are part of traditional culture. They show that different groups of people within society have characteristic ways of behaving and communicating with each other. Cultural patterns and traditions have developed to meet some important need, or in response to a particular environment. Intellectual development and school achievement are both heavily dependent on symbolic activity, and *telling type* instructions. The use of word and number enables the user to refer to, and think about, objects and ideas which are not immediately present. A symbol stands for something other than itself, and the use of symbols greatly enriches our potential for thinking and communicating. It enables us to talk about things that are far distant in space and time, enabling us to bring the past and future into present discourse. Bruner distinguishes between three kinds of thinking. Enactive thinking is that which goes on in muscles, joints and brain when for example, we ride a bicycle, swim or walk upstairs. Most of us would not call this thinking at all. These are, however, activities which have been learned, and information about how to do them is stored somewhere in the nervous system. Iconic thinking is that which goes on when we imagine things – our living room at home, the play we saw last night, the first delivery we witnessed. These are *pictures in the head* which can be experienced quite independently of words. To be able to communicate the experience with any accuracy we need the third kind of thinking, namely, symbolic thinking which depends upon the translation of an image or idea into a symbol. In order to communicate anything about last night's play, or the first delivery we witnessed, we need to be able to translate details of the image into symbols such as stage, actor, etc. In adulthood we engage at various times in enactive, iconic and symbolic thinking, but the ability to do so is a consequence of development. It is often found that practical people who can 'see how to do things' are not very good at instructing anyone else. The instruction may require translating from iconic to symbolic thinking.

Figure 5.1. Baby in incubator, isolated from usual human contact.

Nurses often learn the requirements for a particular procedure from a trolley diagram. The equipment for a lumbar puncture or intravenous infusion is often presented in visual terms and is remembered iconically. Images are relatively inflexible and they can be retained without any real understanding of the purpose of the parts. An alternative method of learning about the requirements for a lumbar puncture and so on, is to use symbolic thinking. This requires some discussion of the technical process involved and an understanding of the necessary steps to perform it. Every trolley need not look exactly alike – what is required is a collection of containers, fluids, swabs, local anaesthetic and the means of administering it all arranged in such a way as to have regard to asepsis, comfort of the patient and so on. Symbolic thinking enables the nurse to be much more adaptable.

The newborn child's experience of his surroundings is probably mainly enactive – bodily sensations and experiences. Babies of two weeks old have shown by their behaviour that they can remember something about their mother's face (Carpenter 1974), and also that they can remember how far away an object was from them (Bower 1974). This seems to indicate that even very young children have the beginnings of iconic thinking.

There remain many unanswered questions about long term development of skills, abilities, inventiveness and ingenuity, mental health, contentment, assurance and sociability. It is, however, now reasonably clear that development depends upon information and experiences that get in from the outside, as well as the unfolding of potential from the inside. Bruner (1964) says development of cognitive ability (that is to think, reason, understand, etc.) is as much from the *outside in,* as from the *inside out.* The midwife is present at the beginning, and by the experiences she is able to provide, and the discussion she is able to have with the mother, may be an important influence in what passes from the *outside in.*

Babies who are nursed in intensive special care units may have particular problems arising out of their isolation (Fig. 5.1). Babies in incubators experience a different quality of care and human contact, from that of a well full term baby. They have less close physical contact, do not experience a diurnal rhythm of light and darkness, hear unusual and monotonous sounds which rarely include the human voice, have a greater variety of caretakers and a wider range of tactile and painful experiences.

Little is known at present of the abilities of the pre-term infant, that is, what he can see, hear, remember and what he selects for attention and so on. It is likely that these abilities need time to develop, but we do not know. It has been shown that the contact between mothers and

Figure 5.2. A sick baby being given extra tactile, visual and kinaesthetic stimulation.

their babies in incubators is remarkably slight, even when visiting is encouraged (Prince, Firlej and Harvey 1978). The midwife who is caring for such babies may be able to provide more normal experiences for them and, above all, encouraging their parents to do likewise. Little will be lost if their neurological apparatus is insufficiently mature to hear or see stimuli which are provided. Their development may be unnecessarily hampered by an absence of stimulation. An experiment in which pre-term babies were given extra tactile, visual, and kinaesthetic stimulation compared very favourably in weight gain and behavioural development with controls who were not so treated (Scarr-Salapatek and Williams 1973) (Fig. 5.2). Other problems associated with small pre-term and ill babies are discussed in Chapter 6. The midwife can play a very important role here in ensuring that contact by parents, and the level and type of stimulation is maintained near to the normal pattern as is compatible with the high standards of physical care so vital to his healthy survival.

REFERENCES

Bayley, N. & Shaefer, E. (1960) *Journal of Genetic Psychology,* **96** pp 61-77.

Bower, T. (1974) Competent Newborns. *New Scientist,* **61** pp 672.

Bowlby, J. (1951) *Maternal Care and Mental Health,* Monograph 3 Geneva: WHO.

Bowlby, J. (1969) Attachment. *Attachment & Loss,* Vil. I. London: Hogarth Press.

Bruner, J. (1964) The Course of Cognitive Growth, *American Psychologist,* **ii,** 1-15.

Carpenter, G. (1974) Mother's Face and the Newborn. *New Scientist,* **61** pp 742.

Davie, R., Butler, N., Goldstein, J.H. (1972) *From Birth to Eleven.* Harlow: Longmans for the National Children's Bureau.

de Licardie, E.R. & Cravioto, J. (1974) Behavioural responsiveness of survivors of clinical severe malnutrition to cognitive demands, in *Early Malnutrition and Mental Development.* Ed. by Cravioto, J., Hambraeus, L., Vahl Guist, B. Swedish Nutrition Foundation.

Fantz, R.L.F. (1966) The Crucial Early Influence: Mother love or environmental stimulation? *American Journal of Orthopsychiatry,* **36** No. 2. pp 330-336.

Forgus, R.H. (1966) *Perception: The Basic Process in Cognitive Development.* New York: McGraw Hill.

Irwin, O.C. (1949) Infant Speech *Scientific American,* **181** pp 22-24.

Jean-Marc-Gaspard Itard (1962) *The Wild Boy of Aveyron,* translated by George & Muriel Humphrey. New York: Appleton Century Crofts.

Kagan, J. & Freeman, M. (1963) *Child Development,* **34** pp 899-911.

Levine, J., Fishman, O. & Kagan, J. (1967) *Society for Research in Child Development.*

Moss, H.A., Robson, K.S. & Pederson, F. (1969) *Developmental Psychology,* **239** - 246.

Prince, J., Firlej, M., Harvey, D. (1978) *Contact between babies in incubators and their caretakers.* In press.

Report on the Care of Children Committee: *The Curtis Report* (1947) London: HMSO.

Richards, M.P.M. (1975) Unpublished lecture delivered at St Charles' Hospital, Ladbroke Grove.

Scarr-Salapatek, S. & Williams, M.L. (1973) The Effects of Early Stimulation on Low-Birth Weight Infants. *Child Development,* **44** No. 1 pp 94-101.

Shields, R. (1962) *Monozygotic Twins.* Oxford: Oxford University Press.

Spitz, R.A. (1945) Hospitalisation. An enquiry into the genesis of psychiatric conditions in early childhood. *Psychoanalytic study of the child,* **1** pp 57-74. New York: International Universities Press.

Thomas, A., Chess, S. & Birch, H. (1970) 'The Origin of Personality'. *Scientific American,* **223** No. 2 pp 102-109.

Tulkin, S. & Kagan, J. (1972) *Child Development,* **43** 30-41.

6

Handicaps

A handicap for a runner in a race is an advantage conferred, or an adverse condition imposed, so that the chances of the competitors are made more nearly equal. An adverse condition, extra weight to be carried, or a delay in starting, is imposed on an individual who has shown evidence of being particularly good. Although the term can be used to mean an advantage, it is more generally applied to the imposition of a disadvantage. Conditions referred to as *handicapping* in infants and children, are always those which seem to weaken the child's chance of survival, or make a satisfactory adaptation to life more difficult. An extremely attractive appearance, or exceptionally high intelligence are not generally regarded as handicaps, although they may militate against satisfactory adaptation in society. Many characteristics of individuals are distributed normally throughout the population, that is to say, most people are to be found in the middle ranges and comparatively few at the low or high end. Take height for example – the average height of 18 year old boys is, at present, 174 cms; very few are less than 160 cms and very few more than 190 cms. Young men at the extremes are faced with a number of difficulties of which their peers of more average height know nothing. They will find it more difficult to buy clothes that they like to fit them, and they will have to pay more for them. The clothing manufacturers mass produce for the average. Social relations may not be so easy either. The short boy may be treated as if he were younger and less capable than he feels – the opposite is true for the very tall. In social relations height is important. Someone we have to look up to in a physical sense is spontaneously attributed with authority and dominance. The short man cannot assume an authoritative role but has to assert himself to achieve it.

The values, standards, ideals and customs of a culture can usually be found to be derived from the norms of that culture. Individuals too far

78

away in either direction from the norm are likely to experience some kind of social pressure. The exceptionally quick learner is often as much of a problem for the teacher in the classroom, as the exceptionally slow one. There are many examples in history of innovatory ideas appearing *before their time* – that is, being too far away from the social and intellectual norms of the time. Advantages and disadvantages have, therefore, to be seen in relation to the norms and values which are generally held in society. It must be remembered also, that these do change – sometimes fairly quickly. A glance through a fashion magazine of 20 or 30 years ago readily shows how ephemeral notions of beauty are.

The survival rate of handicapped infants has increased, together with the general improvement in infant survival rate. Furthermore, medical advances ensure that many survive into adulthood, and may indeed have an average expectation of life. Whether social attitudes and values have changed commensurately to accommodate a wider range of characteristics and abilities is a matter of conjecture. There are a number of hopeful signs. Despite some hypocrisies there is a genuine interest in, and attempt to make provision for, care in the community rather than in an institution. Community care for a child with Down's syndrome for example, is likely to mean care by the family with support from local health and social services, both statutory and voluntary. An absence or inadequacy of this support may contribute to a family succumbing, and the child becoming institutionalised. How far local support is forthcoming will depend quite a lot on prevailing social attitudes.

Discussions and decisions within the hospital about a handicapped baby do need to take into account social policies and conditions outside the hospital. One family may have the material, psychological and spiritual resources to rear unaided a handicapped child, and help him achieve his full potential, whereas another would flounder under such a burden. Some knowledge of local provision is, therefore, essential. Different ethnic and social groups not only have some handicapping conditions which are either peculiar, or more common to them (e.g. Tay-Sachs amongst Jews, spina bifida amongst the Irish) but also probably have specialised attitudes which so far as we can discover have not been the subject of any detailed study. For example in a social group which depends on a good physique for its survival – perhaps a primitive agricultural community – physical handicaps such as talipes or congenital dislocation of the hip, may cause more consternation than mental handicap. A short film called Michael (BFI 1960) shows how happily a boy with Down's syndrome fits into rural farm life in Suffolk. On the other hand, a child with a poor physique but good intellect is likely to experience favourable attitudes in an intellectual and bookish family. It has been shown that some Africans use their bodies in movement and gesture to communicate, more than Europeans do. Clumsiness and psychomotor disabilities are likely to be more apparent, and of greater social significance in such a society than in one where communication depends more on language.

The medical view of a handicap is usually coloured by its long term prognosis, the amount of surgical correction entailed and the course of treatment and management envisaged. A parent's response to an ill or disabled baby may be determined by quite different factors, and it may be helpful here to classify handicaps by criteria other than those normally used in paediatric literature.

Sometimes a mother is aware that there is a risk of her baby being born small or before full term. Her own experience, if she has had previous children, may make her suspicious but it is more likely that she will be aware of the concern that is conveyed, directly or otherwise, by obstetrician or midwife. By no means all mothers realise the implications for the baby of low birth weight. Even if she is not surprised by an early delivery she may nevertheless be unprepared for the possibility of her baby being ill. Mothers of multiple births similarly are sometimes not prepared for small babies. Even so, no one can predict with any accuracy the condition of the baby, or babies, and the drama of the birth is likely to be heightened by the hopes and anxieties that surround it.

Occasionally a baby is stillborn. This poses a considerable number of problems as death for our society is rather as sex was for the Victorians; rarely talked of, surrounded with anxieties and embarrassment taking place secretly behind screens and curtains. Bereavement in these circumstances can rarely find suitable expression because it too, is a source of embarrassment. The rituals associated with the disposal of the dead body serve a number of important functions. A funeral which friends, relatives and neighbours attend, publicly affirms the altered status of the bereaved. A woman who has lost her baby is no longer a mother. It also affords the bereaved some formal outward sign of support. Attending a funeral in some parts of rural Britain is still regarded as a sign of respect for the bereaved family which it would be churlish to withhold. Another custom, now rarely practised, is to invite friends to look at the body in the coffin; the undertaker would leave the lid of the coffin unfastened until it reached the church, in case any mourners wanted to see the corpse. There are no doubt, some fairly material and practical explanations for this practice (for assurance that bodies had not been snatched or exchanged) but it also serves to enable members of the community to acknowledge their involvement and concern. At a psycho-social level such intimate arrangements facilitated an easier communication about death, and a relative freedom from embarrassment.

Some women who have had a stillbirth subsequently complain bitterly that they were never permitted to see their baby. Perhaps not all mothers would like this, but several have expressed an unresolved longing to have done so even if their baby was malformed. Some mothers would have liked to have held their dead baby in their arms, to acknowledge his brief existence in the spontaneous way that is quite appropriate with the newly born. A stillborn baby, although dead, has for months before been a living being, of whom the mother has been aware. He has been growing, moving, been the focus for plans and hopes: his dying may seem the more desperate if the mother is denied the opportunity to touch or see the body, which has for so long been part of herself. It is not suggested that all mothers should see or hold their dead baby, but some have certainly regretted not having been allowed to do so. A short article by a midwife (Warren 1977) poignantly expressed this desire even though she realised her baby was macerated. Her midwife considered it inadvisable, but five months later the author was obviously still wishing she had seen the baby.

People who have not been present at the death of a relative or close friend have sometimes expressed a similar regret. There is a sense of incompleteness which makes mourning a more difficult process. In these cases of intra-uterine death the mother usually notices the absence of movements and realises that her labour will not produce a live baby. The immediate shock of death has often already passed. The unexpected stillbirth when the baby dies during labour or delivery, is a very different matter for both the parents and the staff. The quietness is bizarre. Sudden death tends to paralyse the onlooker. The midwife and obstetrician may have a sudden sense of failure of their professional abilities. The normal happy sequence of behaviour which follows delivery is totally disrupted; the usual words of encouragement, pleasure and admiration of the new baby dry up. The feelings of the staff may be in such disarray that they retreat into functional efficiency which can add to the anguish for the mother. It is a common experience for those associated with death to feel some guilt – was everything done as it should have been? – could things have been otherwise? The mother, bereft and stunned can be totally isolated with no longed-for baby, no words with which to communicate, and no one who can listen, or sit quietly with her. The deepest grief by being unspeakable may continue its corrosive work for years.

Some women, despite the fact that they have subsequently reared healthy children, continue to feel and grieve the loss of a stillbirth. When the subject is mentioned anger and distress are often still felt. One woman, known to us, said that she could hardly bear to think about it twenty years afterwards, and blushing deeply, apologised for having spoken of the event. Another attributed the breakup of her marriage to the fact that neither she nor her husband could deal with nor communicate their profound grief over their loss, possibly due to fear of deepening the wound to their partner even more.

How then can this situation be alleviated? Seeing or holding the baby, already mentioned, is helpful for some parents. For others, giving him or her a name serves the purpose of marking his brief life with some significance. Asking 'What is his name?' would perhaps help the mother to focus her anguish on a real person. Some mothers have been told to forget all about it and go home and start another baby as soon as possible. The implication seems to be that one baby is much the same as any other and the loss can be made good fairly quickly. For some mothers this may be the case although most women seem to recall in considerable detail, not the sameness of events associated with their children, but the differences. The marriage relationship develops and changes, and how the couple feel about each other is likely to be an important factor in their attitude to a new conception. Pregnancies are different too. Events that take place during the nine months contribute to the parents' ideas about the child. Bitter and unresolved grief is hardly a basis to be recommended for embarking on another pregnancy. The refusal to recognise the dead baby as having any personal significance for the mother may mean that she has to contend with free floating grief which she cannot locate in a person or a place. Depression is by no means uncommon in normal postnatal women, and in those who are at home for long periods (Gavron 1966, Lovegrove 1976). To be caught in addition, in a conspiracy to deny the importance of the pregnancy, the birth and death of a child, is highly likely to increase the risk of depression.

Traditionally the burial place has been of great significance. The tomb has been the object of pilgrimage, or of regular attention of some kind – placing of flowers or a wreath. Mothers do not always know the means by which their stillborn babies are disposed of, let alone know where their remains are to be found. 'We felt he had been buried like so much rubbish, with no acknowledgement of his much wanted, brief existence', wrote one mother (Jolly 1975). There has been very little attempt until recently to explore the immediate and long term consequences of stillbirth for a mother. What is clear is that problems associated with bereavement are often not effectively resolved in society as a whole, nor by health professionals (Parkes 1972). Stillbirth is a special case in which emotions associated with both birth and death become intertwined. The mother's body is hormonally prepared for a new life, the breasts fill for an infant who no longer lives. From the comments gleaned from a few mothers and from our own limited experience, this seems to be an area of personal relationships where much more needs to be known. How does the grief reaction differ from that for a person who has been well known? Further information concerning the long and short term effects of a stillbirth on parents, their grief reactions and their mourning processes, as well as the sort of help that is effective, is much needed. Little purpose seems to be served by imposing a taboo on seeing or speaking about the baby.

As this *death taboo* is a very general one in contemporary society it is often difficult for individuals to overcome. This applies as much to health professionals as to the general public. An event which is of great significance to an individual, but is nevertheless forbidden expression does not disappear. It is likely to remain the longer. It is the lot of many of the bereft to become social pariahs. The reason is that few of us know how to talk with them. We fear allowing them to talk as this may expose not only *their* unseemly feelings, but our own as well. To help a mother who has just borne a stillbirth a midwife needs, as well as an empathetic response to the mother, considerable self-understanding. This may come with experience of living, but can certainly be helped through discussion in suitably arranged group conditions. These can give some opportunity for members to reflect on their own intense feelings, some of which may be subject to strongly conditioned reticence.

A midwife who feels compelled to mask her own feelings by efficient busy-ness, is unlikely to be able to offer a mother much understanding if she should ask to hold her dead baby, or rail against the hospital and its staff, or lie mute in bed for her short stay in hospital. Holding the baby immediately after delivery is more practical than later on, when the little body is stiff and cold and has often been the subject of a post mortem examination. Preparing it then for viewing or holding, is a daunting task for anyone. Women who have had a stillbirth are usually discharged quickly from hospital. The presence of more fortunate women may, by providing contrast, exaggerate their grief, although it is likely that the core of the problem is the one already mentioned, namely the inhibitions and social embarrassments surrounding death and the bereaved. Undoubtedly every woman has her own way of contending with the disappointment and misery of stillbirth. Adversities which do not overwhelm can initiate personal growth, but if they are too great they can have a damaging effect on a person's functioning which may be protracted or even permanent. In the last fifteen or twenty years there has been a great interest in the psychological aspects of dying, and bereavement, and a few pioneers like Dr Cecily Saunders have helped, not only to change provisions for care, but considerably altered public and professional attitudes. A similar change of attitude to, and treatment of, parents who have had stillbirths has still to come, although their problems are beginning to be publicly discussed.

About one baby in 40 is born with some kind of handicap. This may be a visible defect, or a disease which is not immediately apparent, for example, cystic fibrosis. The handicap may shorten his expectation of life and may affect his prospects for physical and mental development.

Parents do not always assess their baby by the same criteria as health professionals. A malformation which a paediatrician may regard as easily remediable, may seem quite appalling to the mother and father. On the other hand, the high risk of imminent death associated with some few abnormalities, may not be recognised by the parents unless they are given some special help to come to a realistic appreciation of the fact. One of the authors has had the unhappy experience of trying to convey to a father the seriousness of his baby's respiratory distress. Despite considerable endeavour in emphasising the gravity of the situation, and a refusal to recognise his alternative proposal that 'The baby will be alright', he seemed quite unable to take in such bad news. He was shocked and angry when the baby died. Sometimes the inability to acknowledge the disaster extends further, and the dead baby is treated as if it were still alive. Anthropologists have found in

Figure 6.1. Baby with a cleft lip.

Figure 6.2. Baby with a damaged face.

some cultures where babies are carried on the body, that a dead child is carried by the mother until it stinks.

There is a considerable amount of evidence that handicapped and unusual children, like their normal brothers and sisters, develop emotionally, socially and intellectually better in a family than in an institution. This fact should not lead us to overlook or minimise the problems which some handicapped children can create for their families, perhaps especially the mother. Events in the immediate postnatal period are of crucial importance, but they must be seen as part of a continuing process in which practical advice and help, as well as support and understanding are available from other professions and services to the family of the handicapped child. It is undoubtedly highly desirable for the child that he should have the opportunity of growing up in an affectionate and caring family setting. Should his parents be unable to accept him as an individual who needs their concern and consideration, or even worse, if he is entirely rejected, this can but add a further handicap with which he must contend.

Careful consideration, therefore, needs to go into the question of communicating with the parents in the postnatal period. Disfigurements of the face cannot be hidden and the mother is immediately aware of them. Physical appearance is an important element in interpersonal relations, and in the last two decades there have been several studies demonstrating the psychological importance of physical appearance (Clifford and Bull 1976). Many mothers, especially first mothers, have built up a picture of the lovely baby they are going to have from pictures, advertisements and a selection of the prettiest or most handsome of older children they know. A baby with a large strawberry naevus, port-wine stain, cleft palate and cleft lip, or some other facial disfigurement, may shock the mother deeply (Figs. 6.1 & 6.2). It may be doubly important for such a mother to hold her baby and to feel him. She may not want to look at him, but the early postpartum contact which has been shown to be so important for the development of good relations between mother and baby (Kennell and Klaus 1972) can be through tactile experience and bodily contact.

Prospects for repair and correction involving medical and surgical decisions and procedures, will be discussed with the parents as far as is practicable. The possibilities and likely outcome and plans for treatment, will be communicated by the paediatrician or surgeon. Further discussions by the midwife of what has been said by them may be very helpful to the mother. She may have neither taken in, nor fully understood what has been said. There may be questions which she is apprehensive of putting to the medical staff and undoubtedly she will forget much of what is explained, and communication about the baby, his treatment and future must be a continuing process between staff and both parents. The mother is likely to have many questions to ask and many more for which she cannot find the words. They may remain as amorphous worries which cannot be readily crystalised into language.

A midwife who has built up a relationship with the mother may, if she can spend time with her, learn much about her feelings. This will involve not only listening to what is said, but being aware of the significance of many non-verbal communications. Non-verbal signals can be very subtle. There are the questions and comments which never receive a reply, or which occasion a change of topic. Slight changes of expression, about the mouth and eyes, especially the making or evading of eye contact, convey something of the type and intensity of feeling. A change of posture, a seemingly irrelevant gesture can signal intent, confusion, despair or satisfaction. It often seems to be forgotten in hospital, that communication with someone in bed, is facilitated by sitting by the bed and being within a range of about two feet. The midwife who stands over a patient is in an authoritative position and will be treated as such. Authorities on the whole tell, they do not listen. Patients often say they have not talked to sister because she always seems so busy. This apparent lack of time for talking is often eloquently conveyed by the speed at which people walk. Compare, for example, walking speeds of patients, nursing and medical staff.

A mother's feelings in the puerperium may vitally affect the way in which she handles and manages her baby. These may be of grief for the image of the beautiful normal baby who has not been born to her. There may be anger, depression, guilt, self criticism, aggressive feelings towards the hospital, the midwife or the baby himself. Anger is sometimes strongly expressed by the father. Some of the visually distressing handicaps can be effectively corrected. Extra fingers, bat ears, cleft lip, however, may affect the amount of contact the mother is willing to make with her child in the post-partum period. The infant has a number of ways by which he attracts the mother and keeps in touch with her. Sucking, clinging and following with the eyes, are apparent at birth or shortly afterwards. By these means he can maintain contact with his mother. By crying and smiling he can attract her attention. The way the mother responds to these activities is important for the development of attachment behaviour. The midwife can do much to encourage this. The feeding difficulties of the baby with a cleft lip and cleft palate may distort sucking behaviour, as limb defects may distort clinging. Sometimes a baby with a cleft lip can breast feed satisfactorily, and it is well worth encouraging the mother to try this. The mother may inadvertently add further difficulties to the baby's development of a repertoire of social and attachment behaviour by being unwilling to look at him. Despite these difficulties, however, babies with visible facial defects are very rarely rejected. Most parents will know someone who has had a successful repair so there is good reason to be hopeful.

A recently reported study of the psychological effects of facial deformity in children (Lansdown and Polok 1975) shows that children of school age are remarkably consistent in their judgements of facial malformations. 75 children aged 9–11 in London and Amsterdam consistently judged as least favourable – protruding teeth, next cleft lip, squint, misshapen nose, and bat ears, in that order. In the same study 24 children who had been operated on for correction of cleft lip in 1965 were followed up. Their behaviour and attainment were compared with that of normal children. They were all 7 or 8 years old. On neither of these measures were there any significant differences. One inference to be drawn is that children disadvantaged in their appearance may have compensated by the development of other valued qualities and characteristics. This phenomenon of compensation is not unusual but it does require cultivation, and the parents are the most likely people to be able to encourage it. It is important, therefore, when discussing the baby with the parents to be quite clear that he has, like any other human being, a great variety of needs, for which he is dependent on his parents, and a wealth of potentialities and capacities which require suitable opportunities for their development.

Some authorities are of the opinion that the father is often better able to take a long term view, and more objective approach to the problem of an abnormal baby, while the mother is more likely to be disproportionately concerned with immediacies. Experienced workers with whom we have discussed this have rarely found this to be so. Some fathers, particularly from cultures where the male retains his dominant position in society, feel an abnormal baby to be an unfavourable comment on their manhood. There will, however, in most cases be two parents with whom the midwife is in regular communication. One may help the other, or they may confuse one another. They may be better able to talk things over about their baby in the presence of a third person. Broaching a sensitive topic can be difficult for two people on their own. If embarrassment, or anger is aroused, the only path open to them may be to terminate the interaction. A third person can be used as a sounding board or as someone to hold the balance. A communication which might be difficult for one parent to make directly to the other can be facilitated by being apparently said to the third person. We all make use of this social facilitation and are usually unaware of doing so.

A task of primary importance is that of enabling the parents to develop a close affectionate relationship with their baby. An acknowledgement of the baby as someone with many positive qualities, and of the parents as being responsible and capable, with help, of nurturing these qualities, may go far to achieve that task.

Further difficulties are raised by the baby who has some visible defect which is unlikely to be remediable. Malformations of the central nervous system, spina bifida, hydrocephalus, anencephalus come into this group. In addition to the immediate blow to the hope of having a whole and attractive baby, the parents have an indeterminate period of uncertainty as to the length and quality of the child's life. Parents facing the prospect of caring for a child of limited physical and mental capacity, not only need great personal resources, but all the help they can get from agencies in the community to which they can be introduced before they go home. The isolated and unsupported family is the one which is most likely to succumb to the strain of having a handicapped child. A study by Sheila Hewett (1970) of families of handicapped children in the East Midlands, shows the conflict which is sometimes experienced when professional workers can do nothing of a practical nature. One mother referring to the health visitor, said, 'I was absolutely longing to talk to somebody and every time she came up the road I thought, "Surely she's coming to see me *this* time" – I think she would be helpful if she could . . . but there's nothing they can say'. This is one of many examples given where both mother and professional worker see the *real job* as taking some specific action. Where there is no solution to the problem, and health professionals are sometimes embarrassed at having to acknowledge their inadequacy, contacts are then awkward and tend to be avoided. The patient with a terminal illness in a ward is generally the one most avoided. Yet it might be thought that because medical and nursing aims of restoring him to health have failed, he is in more, rather than less, need of comfort. Much work with the parents and family of a handicapped child entails not solving a problem, but helping them to live with it. This can be done by listening, and showing an understanding of the unhappiness and frustration, but perhaps most of all by sharing the problem. Mothers in particular, who feel they are on their own contending with an unusual baby, and trying to come to terms with their own sometimes destructive feelings, and with the unspoken comments of relatives and neighbours, carry a very heavy burden.

The prognosis and possibilities for the baby have to be dealt with from a medical angle. There may be surgical intervention which provides a long term hope of improvement. In the short term, however, it removes the baby entirely from the mother's care, calls into question her competence as a mother, and disrupts the development of social behaviour between the two. Anything that can be done to maintain the contact between mother and baby may have long term consequences. With some help mothers can often provide much of the routine attention for their babies, even if they are seriously ill or recovering from an operation. There is the risk in hospital that nurses and midwives will take over the maternal role. One mother whose baby was in an incubator said to us, 'I am afraid the nurses will steal my baby'. She was expressing an anxiety often felt but seldom brought to the surface quite so clearly, that the intervention of a nurse between her and her baby might make her relationship with him less close.

Where there is no question of corrective or ameliorative surgery, the parents may face the prospect of caring for a baby with a poor prognosis. Unfortunately on this matter, as on most others with which we are concerned in this chapter, there is little in the way of systematic research which can help in framing a policy or advising parents. Most people would probably agree that caring for a dying child is a most distressing experience. Babyhood and childhood are times for looking forward with hope. Dying is a time of grief and separation. The grief of bereavement is often anticipated by relatives and friends who are aware of the impending death. These incompatible emotions of hope and despair converge most painfully for anyone looking after a dying baby. The incongruity cannot be resolved. The excessive painfulness of the experience probably precludes the possibility of parents being able to express anything of it in words. Extremely painful experiences tend eventually to get repressed into the unconscious, where they are inaccessible to the normal processes of recollection. This almost certainly accounts for the fact that there is very little information available as to how parents cope with the conflicts and confusions aroused by a child with a short life expectation. A recent enquiry concerning visiting by parents to their babies in a special care unit, showed that they had to overcome very high levels of anxiety to visit. Even those parents, however, whose baby died, said they would have been very much against any restriction of visiting, and they did not regret any of the time they had spent with the child (Harper *et al*, 1976).

Parents of the abnormal or ill baby may have their instinctual responses of caring and protectiveness deflected by his appearance and prospects, but they may nevertheless be considerably motivated to do their best for their infant son or daughter. Any parent taking on such a task has a right to the relevant medical information which is available, and to have the assurance that support and help will be forthcoming when they need it.

The birth of a handicapped baby produces multiple insecurities. Even a mother who has had previous children, may have little to guide her as to how to physically handle her new baby. She is likely to wonder whether there are other associated handicapping conditions which she cannot see, or has not been told about. The birth may considerably upset her self-esteem, call into question her integrity as a wife, a mother, and a normal person. She may be unable to resolve a variety of questions in her own mind as to how the baby's siblings will be affected. Each mother will have her own characteristic way of responding, but it would be extraordinary if she did not show some unusual aspects of behaviour. The baby's father may also face a crisis over his self-esteem, integrity and manhood. A handicapped baby often arouses the whole family to self-examination. Difficult relationships between in-laws may explode into acrimonious genetic vilification with angry disappointed grandparents being anything but helpful. Anxiety and doubt may manifest themselves by a ceaseless asking of questions. They may be straightforward requests for factual information, or used as a method of engaging someone's attention. If a question is repeatedly asked, despite an answer having been given, it may mean that the information is so totally unacceptable that it cannot be incorporated into the mother's thought processes. Most doctors and nurses will have had the experience of a patient, or patient's relative, claiming they have never been given an important, but disagreeable piece of information despite proof to the contrary. This often means the information when it *was* given, was so totally unacceptable to them that it has been subconsciously rejected. Anxieties are sometimes very difficult to put into words. All but the most articulate may not be asking quite the question they want to ask. They may be simply putting in a plea that someone should spare time to listen. Constant demands may be not for answers, but for someone to listen to anger, grief, self-accusation, despair or the blaming of others which may include the hospital, the obstetrician, or the midwife. This may be a testing out period too, in which the mother will find out who has the resources to help her, by sharing her unhappiness and making themselves available to her.

In most cases it will be impossible for a clear prognosis to be given. The early months and years will be a wait-and-see period, with alternating hopes and fears. When future development is uncertain there is every reason to suggest to the parents, that the more interesting and stimulating the child's life can be made the better hope he will have for maximising his potential abilities.

There is another class of handicapped babies. These are the ones in which no problem is immediately obvious. Many mentally subnormal children have shown no signs at birth of their handicapped status. The infant with Down's syndrome may not look abnormal to his parents, although the condition is usually suspected by hospital staff. The question then arises as to when, how, and by whom, the parents should be told. Parents have sometimes been left in ignorance until the child was more than two years old; some have discovered by accident. Others have been told almost immediately after the birth. It is not unknown for parents to have been misinformed that their baby has Down's syndrome. The debate as to the best time to give information derives from two opposing views. One is that where the diagnosis is certain, the parents have a right to have the information as soon as is practicable. The other view is that a normal loving relationship between mother and baby will have a better chance of development, without the intrusion of such information, and that it will be easier for the mother to accept the baby with his problem, after some social behaviour is established between the two.

An enquiry made of the mothers of 71 children with Down's syndrome born in the years 1950–56 in Edinburgh, showed that there was more satisfaction about the timing of their being told when this was done early than when it was done late (Drillien & Wilkinson 1964). 81.3 per cent of mothers who were informed before the baby was 10 days old said they were satisfied with the timing as compared with 22.2

per cent of them who were told after two years. It must be remembered, however, that these are mothers who have kept their babies. We do not know what proportion of all women who were told early rejected their babies. This certainly happens from time to time, and the damaging effect of this on the child's development makes it a serious consideration. The parents who leave their baby in hospital to be cared for, may be parents who would be unable to deal with stressful information at any time. As we have discussed elsewhere however, the first few days after birth are particularly sensitive to interferences. In any case it might be thought advisable to have the benefit of a chromosome analysis, which takes about four days, before making a pronouncement. (A diagnosis *can* be made within 24 hours from bone marrow. It seems doubtful whether this will be widely used for the diagnosis of Down's syndrome.)

Outward appearances can be misleading. In the Edinburgh study mentioned above, nearly half the mothers said they realised there was something seriously wrong with their baby, before they were told. Five claimed to have recognised the stigmata when they first saw him. Retrospective information of this sort always has to be treated with great caution. There is incontravertible evidence that the human memory is extremely unreliable, and that we all tend to recall things which make sense in the light of later events, and we also recall *facts* which put us in a favourable light. On both these grounds mothers may recall having realised their child was unusual, rather earlier than was the case. A prospective study, that is one which keeps account of events as they happen, is needed to check on this kind of material.

There are, of course, parents who either observe peculiarities in their baby, or notice that nursing and medical staff behave unusually to the infant or to them. If the mother has not been informed and asks questions, it will not create an attitude of trust if she is fobbed off with some deceptive answer. Patients of every kind ought to be able to have complete trust in hospital staff, and to know that they are truthful. This is doubly important for parents of handicapped children, who will have to resort to professional advice and guidance more frequently than most. Doubts which are sown by their being misled on one occasion, may take a long time to dispel, as will the memory of a lack of sympathy or unkindness. There may be a period when, like the mother, the staff feel that the baby's appearance does arouse their suspicions, but perhaps it is better for them to insist that there is a period of ambiguity, until a chromosome analysis can be done. Parents are likely to be reluctant to acknowledge the fact that they have a handicapped baby. This can result in their not *taking-in* information they are given. It is important, therefore, that whoever tells them makes the condition of the baby quite clear and unequivocal. It is no kindness in the long run to allow ambiguity or false hope to creep in.

There is likely to be some agreed hospital policy on the matter of relaying information. When the diagnosis is confirmed with the parents, this should be given, together with some details of prognosis. At the same time, or very shortly afterwards, a careful explanation of the services that are available through the health and social services, and voluntary agencies can also be discussed. Perhaps most important is discussion about the positive aspects of the baby, and the important role the parents have to play in helping to make available to him the best facilities. Often enough parents of special or unusual children, have found their role as parents eroded by *experts*. They need the assurance that they can depend on getting help of the sort that will suit them and their family and that the *experts* will be available to help and advise as necessary.

The mentally retarded children who do relatively well, do so because their parents are caring, observant, responsive, and treat the child with respect and encouragement, setting their sights reasonably realistically. Some of the ground work for this, can be done during the puerperium, and the midwife can often teach some important lessons by her example. Some years ago it was confidently proclaimed by many doctors, that a child with Down's syndrome would never be able to learn to read or write. Many devoted teachers of the mentally handicapped have demonstrated the falsity of this assumption. The diary of Nigel Hunt published in 1967 is written by a young man with Down's syndrome who had been lovingly tutored by his mother.

Conveying bad news is never a pleasant task, and most of us avoid it when we can. Such information is probably better given initially by someone known to the parents, so that important features of their social circumstances are taken into account. A midwife who has looked after a woman during the antenatal period, and labour, and has made a good relationship with her, may be an appropriate person to introduce the parents to the fact that the baby has some abnormality which will affect his development. Some preliminary discussion of this sort, may help the parents to derive more benefit from their interview with the paediatrician, who will go into more detail and also be able to deal with long term prospects, and to give parents some idea of what lies ahead, as well as the services which are available. The social worker is an important member of the team, who will have more detailed information about the family, and is particularly skilled in dealing with the emotional difficulties arising.

The report of a working party of the National Association of Mental Health on 'The Birth of an Abnormal Child: Telling the Parents' (*Lancet* 1971) drew attention to the fact that some experienced workers advocate telling the father first. In the immediate post natal period, a father may be more stable than his wife and may appreciate the opportunity to be the first to talk with her about their baby. The report emphasises that on no account should he be used to transfer information which must come direct from a well informed member of the staff – normally the paediatrician.

The father however, is often bewildered and overwhelmed and making him party to such unwelcome information may be a great burden to him. As it is to be hoped that both parents will help and encourage the child, and each other, there seems much to be said for telling them both at the same time.

Abnormalities of the eyes and ears may not be apparent in the first two weeks of life. If defects are discovered by hospital staff, some debate may arise as to whether there is an immediate need to inform the parents. A similar question arises in conditions which may improve spontaneously, such as Erb's palsy. On the one hand it may be thought a disservice to the parents to give them cause for worry, when they are first embarking on settling down with their new baby – a task which comes smoothly to only a lucky few – and things may improve. On the other hand even minor sensory defects do effectively reduce the range and quality of stimulation to which a child can respond. This may affect his speed and pattern of development. Where parents are aware of a deficiency, they might also be able to compensate for it. For example if a baby is blind, or has poor vision, he needs to get more information about his surroundings by hearing and touch, and to develop these two modalities effectively. Were parents informed they could be helped to provide a richer and more varied range of experiences than might otherwise occur.

For a mother who has some difficulty in handling her new born baby, and gets readily upset, it may be better not to give her further cause for agitation. Generally, however, people manage situations better when they are informed than when they are not. If information about any adverse condition is given, it should be associated with possible corrective or ameliorative action which parents can take, and some outline of the prospects for the future.

Every newborn infant has a unique arrangement of innumerable traits and qualities. The baby who is described as handicapped lacks some feature, or characteristic, which is highly valued in our society. How far other features and characteristics can be developed in compensation, and how far he can be accepted as a valued human being, will depend on the environment in which he is reared. Whether he learns to think of himself as a whole person with an abnormality, or as an abnormal, second rate personality will depend on a variety of factors. For example, the way his parents and others accept him, the provision that is made available to help him develop his own special skills and abilities, and the social values that are daily and hourly communicated directly and inadvertently in casual conversations, in newspapers and television around him, all have an effect. By appreciating some of the problems the parents may face, the midwife can play an important part in giving information, sharing discussion and helping with appropriate emotional support.

REFERENCES

British Film Institute: (BFI) Experimental Production Board 1960 by Heather Sutton. Available from Concord Films, Ipswich.

Clifford, B. & Bull, R. (1976) *The Psychology of Personal Identification.* London: Routledge.

Drillien, C.M. & Wilkinson, E.M. (1964) Mongolism – When should parents be told? *British Medical Journal,* **2** pp 1306-7.

Gavron, H. (1966) *The Captive Wife.* London: Penguin.

Harper, Rita, Sia, C., Sokal, S., Sokal, M. (1976) *Journal of Paediatrics,* **89** No. 3 pp 441-445.

Hewett, S. (1970) *The Family & the Handicapped Child.* London: Allen & Unwin.

Hunt, N. (1967) *The World of Nigel Hunt.* Chichester: Darwen Finlayson.

Jolly, H. (1975) The Heartache on facing the facts of the stillborn baby. *The Times,* 3 December 1975.

Kennell, J.H., Jerauld, R., Wolfe, H., Chesler, D., Kreger, N.C., McAlpine, W., Steffa, M. & Klaus, M. (1974) *Developmental Medicine & Child Neurology,* **16** pp 172-179.

Lansdown, R. & Polok, L. (1975) A Study of the Psychological Effects of Facial Deformity in Children. *Child Care, Health & Development.* **1** No. 2 pp 85-91.

Lovegrove, S. (1976) Stuck at Home. London: BBC Publications.

Parkes, C.M. (1972) *Bereavement: Studies of Grief in Adult Life.* London: Tavistock Publications.

National Association of Mental Health (1971) The Birth of an Abnormal Child: Telling the Parents. *Lancet,* **2** pp 1075-1077.

Warren, P. (1977) *Nursing Mirror,* **144** No. 8 p. 60.

7

Antenatal events

During pregnancy a woman prepares herself for a completely new role. The first pregnancy means modifying a wife and worker role, to accommodate to a mother role. Subsequent pregnancies entail changing from the mother of one child to becoming the mother of two. Appropriate role behaviour means living up to expectations and demands of society as they are manifested through neighbours, relatives, newspaper and television. There is universal recognition of the mother role, and little ambiguity about what constitutes proper role behaviour. A good mother is required to care for her baby, to feed, clothe and keep him warm. She is expected to provide opportunities for his physical, intellectual, emotional and social development. Most women become progressively aware of these requirements which will be made of them when their baby is born, and put considerable thought and planning into equipping themselves for their new role.

Human beings have long, if selective, memories, and there will be many such memories for the pregnant woman to revive, stemming from her experiences of her own mother, and others with whom she has had an important relationship. She is likely to remember consciously or otherwise her own mother; the mother's attitudes to her daughter are likely to become part of her own attitudes to her coming baby. If she had an unsatisfactory relationship with her mother she may hope she will manage things in a better way. If her own early life was contented she is likely to accept the idea that she will get on well with her baby, without much question. Much of the memory of early experience may become distorted with the passage of time but the feelings associated with the memories will nevertheless be real. Recollections of things past are likely to be interwoven with hopes, fantasies and fears about the future.

Harlow's experiments (Harlow and Harlow 1966) with baby rhesus monkeys reared with artificial mothers have been mentioned elsewhere in this book. These monkeys who had grown up without a real mother, and without any experience of another of their own species, were very difficult to mate. The few females who did become pregnant were hopeless mothers. They neglected and ill treated their babies.

In a study done at St. Thomas' Hospital it has been found that women who had been separated from their mothers in the early years, had more difficulty in adjusting to their maternal role, and experienced more problems not only with their babies but with their marriages (Frommer 1973). This study provides support for the idea that some aspects of motherhood are transferred from one generation to the next in quite subtle ways. Some girls not only have a better relationship with their fathers than their mothers; they may also identify more with their fathers. That is, they aspire to being more like their father than their mother. Masculine traits of ambition, assertiveness, activity and self-confidence have become more socially acceptable in women in the past twenty or thirty years. It is believed that the daughter who has identified with her father may find more difficulty in adapting to the pregnant role. She may postpone the starting of a family until later than is usual. Some psychoanalysts (Menninger 1943) claim that psychological masculinity and physiological femininity cannot go together happily. This view does seem to overlook the fact that having and caring for a baby requires not the passivity, submissiveness, and receptivity which are claimed to characterise the typically female personality, but considerable forward planning, energy and vigour. Past experience of intimate relationships affect a woman's feelings about herself, by providing her with models and referrants.

Psychological development is a long and continuous process. Early experience is of very great importance, and learning goes on throughout life. Societies vary in their attitudes to pregnancy and motherhood. Some societies for example have a place of very high esteem for the pregnant woman, and delivery is thought of as a joyful event. Infertility is often regarded as a curse, or due to some evil supernatural intervention. There is likely to be an easy acceptance of the pregnant and maternal role in such a culture. In our own society attitudes to pregnancy are not so straightforward. The first pregnancy often means relinquishing a job, and the financial independence that goes with it. Social evaluation of people derives in part from their income, and one of the damaging aspects for anyone who is unemployed is the loss of status suffered. By no means all women do give up work; the point is that it is quite permissible to do so and this affects attitudes to pregnant women.

Another area of conflict which has emerged in this century is the association of pregnancy with medical care and hence with illness. The first antenatal hospital bed was provided in Edinburgh in 1902 (Donald 1972). From an obstetric point of view, the developments which followed were highly desirable and no-one would want to return to the high maternal and infant mortality rates of the past. The fact that a considerable amount of antenatal care is provided in a hospital setting, however, inadvertently reinforces the view that pregnancy is pathological. Rosengren (1961) found that women who regarded pregnancy as an illness, have significantly longer labours. This can be interpreted as showing that the illness role carries with it expectations of behaviour which the subject endorses. Margaret Mead (1950) in her anthropological studies has found that in some cultures morning sickness is expected for primiparae only, in some it is always expected, and in others it is regarded as abnormal. The numbers of women experiencing morning sickness varies with social expectations. Recent developments in obstetrics can only strengthen the association between pregnancy and illness. Pregnancy is *diagnosed,* there may be some discussion about a *therapeutic* abortion, an amniocentesis to make a *diagnosis* of the condition of the fetus, ultrasound cephalometry which involves some medico-technical procedures, and finally delivery itself has become mystified in medical technology. Pregnancy, which in some societies is seen as the peak of female vigour, health and good fortune, is in the advanced societies a confusion of low status, illness, pleasurable anticipation and fulfilment.

Role conflict often produces a state of inactivity at best, depression at worst. If we occupy two roles at the same time and they make equally strong but different demands, this can result in chronic indecision and inactivity. The person in such a position is often confused not only over what to do, but also unsure whom she is. Some women avoid the role conflict by avoiding pregnancy altogether. Ellen Peck's *The Baby Trap* (1973) is a spirited attack on what has been described as the myth of motherhood. The myth is the idealised family, the carefree mother and the beautiful babies, as presented by the food and clothing manufacturers' advertisements, the women's magazines and some of the material published by the health educators. The reality behind the myth is rather different as we know from discordant families, unhappy distraught mothers and neglected injured children.

Another reality is that the improvements in the position of women have in some ways made their lives more difficult. They have more freedom of choice. Any choice point can become a conflict point. Ann Oakley (1975) has shown that in 1971, 60 per cent of women who stopped work did so because of pregnancy, whereas in the 1930s and 40s the usual reason they gave up work was marriage. This means that the first pregnancy is for many women a time of considerable identity crisis. Ann Oakley reports a young pregnant woman as saying 'I can picture myself going out to work but I can't picture myself looking after a baby. . . I'd like the experience of having a baby and then I'd like to give it to someone else to look after and go out to work . . . It's very boring at home. I won't be able to talk to anyone. . . I'm scared of everything.'

Ellen Peck's solution to the identity conflict is to recommend avoidance of the motherhood role altogether. For many women this is not a suitable answer: they really want babies. A few women can perhaps, like Ellen Peck, dichotomise the problem into either motherhood, or social and economic freedom and independence. Many would prefer to work towards a society where bearing and rearing children can be integrated more smoothly into an active social and economic life.

Dana Breen (1975) draws attention to two contrasting assumptions about pregnancy which underlie some particular studies and much of our thinking about the state. These two assumptions she calls the *hurdle* and the *development* assumption. *Hurdle* thinkers consider pregnancy as a period of deviation from normality, with a return to some former state when it is all over. The *hurdle* concept is implicit in such statements as 'All pregnant women are slightly unstable', 'Several researchers find pregnancy is associated with an increased neuroticism score'. The suggestion is that when the pregnancy is over stability and a low neuroticism score will reassert themselves.

Development thinkers on the other hand, look at it as a phase of maturation and growth, which results in a new and more elaborate organisation of the personality. Adolescence as a developmental phase has attracted more interest than has pregnancy. There are some parallels. The adolescent has to contend with rapid inner physiological and psychological changes, and at the same time changes in psychological and social demands made of him by others.

It is a period of considerable role conflict – is he an adult or child – dependent or independent? Both the adolescent and those with whom he lives, learns, and works, change their views and behaviour about him from hour to hour. There is abundant evidence of the behavioural consequences of the conflict experienced during adolescence, but the great majority can eventually integrate their inner experience with external demands and opportunities, and emerge as more developed, integrated and competent personalities. In pregnancy too, there are inner physiological and psychological changes, which coincide with changing expectations by others. The role conflict between wife, worker, mother, independent or dependable person, is likely to be experienced as some sort of crisis. A crisis can be seen as the point at which established patterns of functioning are found to be ineffective. Its resolution comes about with the discovery of new effective modes of thinking, feeling and behaving. The identity crisis may begin some time during pregnancy, and continue for a considerable time after the baby is born. Behaviourally we need a single term to cover the four episodes of pregnancy, childbirth, puerperium and early motherhood. For want of an appropriate word let us call the period the *Maternaliza-tum*. It begins with fertilisation, and is complete when the woman has adjusted the integration of her maternal role with her total personality. This process needs a lot of experience and learning. In less advanced societies where girls and young women take part in the care of other people's babies, much of the necessary experience is acquired before pregnancy. Few girls in our present society have any experience of handling small babies and little time is given to cultivating parenting attitudes in boys and girls at school.

There are a number of studies which show how isolated and depressed women at home with their small children feel. Hannah Gavron's *The Captive Wife* and *Stuck at Home* by Susan Lovegrove are two such examples. It is now emerging that a considerable number of women are depressed in the antenatal period. A Swedish study (Nilsson 1970) found significant psychological disturbance in 25-30 per cent of women attending antenatal clinic. Results are awaited from a similar study now being carried out in the antenatal clinic at University College Hospital, London.

While the problems of the young woman, isolated by her housekeeping and childminding role, have been acknowledged for some time, it has perhaps not been so readily recognised that the dispiriting, debilitating problems, perhaps arising out of role change and personal conflict, are present in a proportion of women antenatally.

Few midwives would feel competent to diagnose psychiatric problems but if these findings are replicated in other antenatal clinics it is plainly of importance that they should be able to do so. We have elsewhere referred to the midwife's role in the continuity of care, and it is in the antenatal clinic that this function should begin, and here that she can start a relationship which can continue until after the baby is born.

Improvements in medical care require increasing specialisation and the effects of this can be experienced by the woman in the antenatal clinic as a series of discreet interests. Her antibodies, weight, baby's head size concern individual people and between them all 'she' is lost. Some women have complained that the only thing that anyone seems the slightest bit concerned about is the baby. One woman said 'As far as they (at an antenatal clinic) are concerned I'm just a vehicle for carrying this baby about – no thoughts, no feelings of my own – nobody asks how I am.' Few sacrifices are made without resentment. When expectant mothers are made to feel that they have some sacrificial duty to their babies they may subsequently be less able to deal with them without hostility. They will have been dutiful but disliked it. To some extent we are all affected by the *we-must-like-babies* folklore. The myth itself often prevents realistic expression of dissatisfaction with the pregnancy. This may be one of the factors underlying depression in the antenatal period. Perhaps midwives should have more training and practice in the management of aggressive and hostile expressions. It is a fairly normal response to feel alarmed if someone speaks destructively or even resentfully of their baby but a midwife is in a very good position to help a woman to recognise her own feelings and perhaps to help her make use of them for her personal development.

A woman in her thirties pregnant for the first time said of herself at the antenatal clinic 'I'm surprised at myself. We've waited such a long time for this baby and now it's coming I'm not so thrilled. Everyone else in the family is very excited and I seem to be dragging my feet over it all.' After a little more discussion the midwife was able to say 'Perhaps you feel as if you are being taken over?' She agreed and they were able to proceed to talk about feelings of resentment at the loss of autonomy.

A proportion of pregnancies end in an abortion. In 1971 for 74 pregnancies that produced a child it is estimated that there were 15 which ended in a spontaneous abortion and 11 which were medically terminated (Lafitte 1972). The miscarriage of a much wanted baby can occasion a marked grief reaction. Several writers have suggested that spontaneous abortion can result from the inability to resolve the inevitable conflict of being pregnant. Jean Hanford (1968) has suggested that there are two stages in resolving this pregnancy conflict. Even when the pregnancy is wanted the emotional stress arising from the adaptations which have to be made, produce a rise in the blood levels of histamine and steroids. As the pregnancy proceeds psychological defence and development take place and the physiological response is lessened. For some women who experience intense conflict, however, the psychological adaptation is insufficient. The irregularity of corticosteroid levels then continue and this can damage the fetus and can lead to spontaneous abortion, prematurity and fetal malfunctioning. This theme of damage being caused to the fetus by emotional stress and psychological conflict has been expanded by Pasamanick in his proposition that there is a continuum of reproductive casualty. We will return to this later in the chapter.

There may be some reason for apprehension about the condition of the fetus during the course of a wanted pregnancy. An amniocentesis may be contemplated. It is very important that both parents fully understand what the procedure involves. Lay people complain with considerable regularity that medical personnel do not make themselves understood and do not listen, or do not make themselves available, to their patients. (For a more detailed examination of this problem the reader is referred to a collection of papers called *Medical Encounters* edited by Horobin & Davis). Any consent to operation or invasive treatment is intended to be informed consent. Where the question of giving consent arises it is doubly important that the midwife should spend time elucidating the procedure and its purpose and to deal sympathetically with whatever enquiries the patient or her husband may wish to make.

The result of the amniocentesis may lead to the recommendation of an abortion. Nobody has to have an abortion and no doctor, nurse or midwife is compelled to have anything to do with it if she or he has conscientious objections. There are many people who may have moral misgivings without being conscientious objectors. On one hand there is a biologically scientific attitude to the problem which does not acknowledge that any moral issue exists. On the other is the view that the calculated destruction of any form of life is immoral, if not sinful and can never be countenanced. Most people are probably somewhere between the two extreme views and could be persuaded that on some occasions an abortion is absolutely right and on others absolutely wrong.

The pregnant woman is not only the carrier of a fetus. She may be the mother of other children, somebody's wife, a neighbour, a daughter; she is part of a matrix of human relationships of which the fetus will become a part. It is this total web of relationships and the rights, demands, expectations which they involve which often have to be weighed in the balance when therapeutic abortion is being considered.

The majority of recommendations to abortion, and requests of women for it, are carried out. Reaction to abortion varies. A Norwegian study (Kolstad 1957) of 897 women reports that 82.5 per cent were glad without reserve. 9.8 per cent were satisfied but doubtful, 3.8 per cent were not happy but realised the abortion had been necessary. 3.7 per cent were repentent. A total of 4.3 per cent had some serious mental disturbance. Similar studies generally show the majority are satisfied but with a very small percentage experiencing some long term mental problem. So far as we are aware no study has yet been done which adequately takes into account the original motivation for the abortion. In view of what has already been said about role conflict and its effect on functioning, abortion even when induced, can be seen as a conflict resolution.

Where amniocentesis or ultrasound have revealed an abnormality informed counselling will be essential. Some problems are known to be much more likely in families where they have already occurred – for example with *spina bifida*. The risks of recurrence of genetic abnormality can sometimes be mathematically calculated. In the end, however, no parents can be assured that their next pregnancy will be satisfactory, nor can they be certain that it will not be. Nothing is certain; it is the parents who have to weigh the risks of failure against the possibility of success. In order to do this they need the most accurate information that is available and ample opportunity to discuss the pros and cons. A well informed and trusted midwife who knows not only the biological factors involved but something of the social background, the hopes and fears of both parents, can serve as an invaluable guide in the process of arriving at a decision.

Obstetricians and midwives, it is often emphasised, deal with two people at a time. While the mother is adjusting to her pregnant role and thinking about her new baby and how she will behave as a mother, the fetus is developing at an extremely rapid rate. Growth is never again so fast. The uterus accords considerable protection from external stimuli to the fetus, but this is to a very large extent offset by its extreme sensitivity. When growth is very rapid stimuli may have a disproportionately powerful effect. It is now well established that a variety of agents which affect the mother also affect the developing fetus. Drugs, smoking, inappropriate diet, radiation, infections, pollutants have all been incriminated in fetal damage. There is also clear evidence that psycho-social factors experienced by the mother affect fetal development.

Studies with animals have the advantage that conditions can be precisely controlled. During the 1930s the injection of certain chemicals and hormones or the deprivation of vitamins to pregnant mammals increased the incidence of various malformations in the offspring. It was suggested that each species or strain had genetic *potentialities* for malformation which are *facilitiated* by exposing the unborn animal to an adverse intrauterine environment. Pregnant animals exposed to anxiety in the form of fear of an electric shock (which is never given) have infants who are timid and disinclined to explore.

Pregnant laboratory mice have been observed to miscarry if the mother perceives the smell of a strange male on the nesting material. These two examples show that fertility can be reduced or offspring impaired by psychological events (that is where the influence is by way of the mother's sensory perceptions).

There is a variety of studies which relate overcrowding in mammals to reproductive difficulty. Animals, however, are not human beings and it would be unwise to assume that the human fetus is exposed to similar risk without further evidence.

There is a pronounced association of socio-economic status with the incidence both of obstetric problems (Butler 1969) and with low levels of intelligence and achievement (Vernon 1969). The perinatal mortality survey found that the reading scores of children at seven years of age whose mothers smoked during pregnancy were significantly lower than those who did not.

Closely related to socio-economic status is population density and this is known to be associated with obstetric problems and with child behaviour problems. Many factors are likely to be involved here both pre- and post-natally. Overcrowded rodent mothers however, produce infants with impaired learning ability, increased emotionality and increased timidity (Keeley 1962).

Stott (1963) has shown that infant ill health, malformation, defect of temperament and mental subnormality form a syndrome which is highly related to stress in pregnancy. The stress he has investigated was occasioned by the experience of housing difficulties, marital infidelity during the pregnancy or bereavement. The idea that emotional upheaval for the mother affects fetal development is an old one. It had been abandoned as being unscientific (presumably because the maternal and fetal vascular and nervous systems are quite separate) and has only been reinstated in the fairly recent past.

Pasamanick and Knoblock (1966) have proposed that there is a continuum of reproductive casualty. They suggest that an adverse event during the antenatal period may have an effect on the fetus ranging from fetal or neonatal death through a series of sublethal but handicapping conditions, including learning and behaviour problems. It is suggested that a factor which is known to increase the risk of fetal death (for example rhesus incompatibility) is likely in milder forms to produce a handicapping condition. Likewise a number of mildly disadvantaging factors may be cumulative and manifest their effects in physical or psychological abnormality. The continuum can be represented in the following figure (Fig. 7.1).

Although there is evidence to support the general thesis that a wide range of physical and psychological events impinging on the mother affect the developing fetus and affect it in some graduated way, the details of the continuum have yet to be researched in detail.

In the diagram on p. 107 it will be seen that conditions to the left of the line are physiologically assessable while those to the right become apparent only through behaviour.

Behaviour is seen to be more sensitive an indicator of prenatal adversity than is physiology. The effects of drugs, prolonged anxiety, infection and so on, on the fetus may be insufficient to affect the infant's morphological structure but may, nevertheless affect neural tissues during their development and hence affect learning ability, responsiveness and long term behaviour.

The idea of a continuum of reproductive casualty is important for the midwife for two major reasons. It suggests that a wide range of physical and psychological events can affect fetal development. It also puts physical and psychological development of the fetus in a coherent and continuous relationship.

The 1970s have seen a great growth of interest in community health and self-help. The DHSS consultative document Prevention and Health: Everybody's Business (1976) summarised much of the thinking on the matter. The midwife in her care of the antenatal mother can play an important part in encouraging community health and self help by including in antenatal classes an education programme.

Antenatal preparation varies from district to district and may be undertaken by a variety of professionals. The Court Report (Report of the Committee on Child Health Services 1976) made a plea for more information to be made available about the function and achievements of parentcraft classes associated with antenatal clinics. Parentcraft however, is not the only education endeavour undertaken during the

Figure 7.1. Diagrammatic representation of Pasamanick's continuum of reproductive casualty.

antenatal period, and here we summarise, and comment on, some of the factors which are concerned. It would be wrong to suggest that this is an exhaustive summary and equally wrong to suggest that all antenatal clinics follow the same pattern. There is no nationally agreed curriculum; so much depends upon the local interests and enthusiasms.

Most antenatal classes have high informational content. Few women have any detailed knowledge about the growth of the fetus and antenatal education provides a good opportunity to discuss fetal growth, the changes in maternal metabolism and the requirements for the maintenance of optimal health of mother and fetus. In the course of such discussion the value of antenatal visits can be made clear. Later in the pregnancy information about feeding and breast preparation is often included. In view of the findings of Eastham *et al.*, (1976) mentioned in Chapter 2 that over half the 200 women in his survey had made up their minds about preferred method of feeding before the pregnancy, the timing of the presentation of this material needs careful consideration. There is a case for thinking that if attitudes to feeding are to be influenced, the earlier breast feeding is discussed the better.

Some preparatory classes include information about the process of labour, and guidance as to what the mother might expect in the way of management during labour, particularly regarding types of pain relief available. In some cases this is combined with a tour of the hospital and labour ward, so that the strange environment is made less threatening when labour does begin.

In addition practical training is often given about relaxation or psychoprophylaxis. The husbands are sometimes included at this stage. Many people take the view that a woman's husband is likely, if she requests his company, to be a good source of moral support during labour. Some are of the opinion that as a joint parent he has a right, if he wishes, to be present at the birth. The current practice in most hospitals seems to be to allow husbands into the labour ward if their wives wish it, and on the understanding that they will leave if requested.

There is the hope, although as yet little evidence to support it, that the parenting role of the father will be encouraged by his being involved as fully as possible during the pregnancy, labour, and delivery. The Court Report (*Fit for the Future* - 1976 p. 115) has this to say: 'A sense of responsibility and partnership is also more likely to be developed if parents are enabled and encouraged to discuss with their advisors the arrangements for the baby's birth'.

Discussion of the sort envisaged here needs to cover not only practical matters but feelings and attitudes of both parents to the coming baby and some consideration of the father's role.

There is probably, in most antenatal preparation classes, an inadequate recognition of the emotional adjustments required of both parents and little discussion on the matter. Referring to fathers one midwife is reported as saying 'They can make a sort of barrier between the midwife and the mother... And, of course, they faint.' (*Radio Times*, 19–25 March 1977, p. 68.)

This seems to dismiss fathers as having no place at the birth of their children. A further extract from the Court Report reads 'This report would also like to see a further study of prenatal care with clearer guidance on what advice parents need during the antenatal period and how best to give it' (*Fit for the Future* - 1976 p. 117).

'The once forbidden subject of "pain" must be freely discussed'

(McKenna 1976). There has in the past been some thinking that women suffered pain because they had been led to expect it. The devoted practice of antenatal exercises which it was believed would lead to a painless childbirth often led to bitter disappointment, a rapid crumbling of morale and a fear that the pain signified abnormality during labour. There are so many variables in culture, education and attitudes of an antenatal group that it requires a skilled teacher to respond to all needs.

The Court Report is concerned by the possibility of conflict between the hospital and the community professionals giving the classes. Many midwives have not had the opportunity to develop their teaching skills since qualifying, and pupil midwives often lack details which our sophisticated society demands. Health visitors may have had only twelve weeks obstetric training, so although trained to educate, often lack the wealth of practical experience needed for the session of teaching about labour.

The future course of labour and its outcome are unknown. The majority will have normal deliveries but a small minority will need highly specialised care. All these eventualities cannot easily or beneficially be discussed in the group as a whole. Some information about the range of analgesics, their method of administration, the likely effects on both mother and baby, are sometimes discussed.

In the past decade there have been innumerable books, leaflets, television and radio programmes on aspects of childbearing. Parents are becoming better informed. The antenatal classes can capitalise on this information but also need to give special consideration to the less well informed mother and father. Patients who have had their babies often display a great fund of goodwill to the hospital staff and to other mothers. Some would undoubtedly be willing to come to antenatal classes to give the consumer's side of the picture.

The antenatal period is a time of change for all members of the family. The changes in the social role of women have been accompanied by considerable changes in the role of men. Many expect to participate in the care and upbringing of their children. Ours is now a multiracial society, however, and it must be remembered that some immigrants fairly newly arrived in the United Kingdom come from a very different cultural background where the male and female roles follow the traditional pattern of being almost entirely separate. Perhaps nowhere is this separation more clearly marked than in the bearing and caring for babies. Men from traditional societies would probably find a close association with the proceedings of an antenatal clinic embarrassingly novel. Their wives are unlikely to welcome any sudden change in behaviour either.

Nevertheless all couples, immigrant or indigenous will, during the antenatal period undergo some change in their relationship in anticipating the baby's arrival. The first pregnancy means a modification for the husband to a husband-and-father role.

Some men marry in order to be mothered and cared for. The need to share the motherly person they married may not be entirely welcome, nor is adjustment particularly easy. The relationship between sex and parenting drives has not been systematically explored. It is generally assumed that the 'natural' state of affairs is that the sex drive is stronger in men and the parenting drive stronger in women. Masters & Johnson (1966) have produced evidence which calls the former assumption into question. The parenting drive may be largely learned. Women with no experience of babies seem to have little 'natural' gift to guide them. Men often seem quite as strongly motivated to have children as women do. These two elemental forces of the family, sex and parenting, are not always equally valued by both partners. 'I married a lovely, sexy girl – then she turned into someone's mother . . .' reads a comment from a marriage guidance counsellor's client. The sentiment is repeatedly expressed by Michael Caine in the film '*Alfie*'.

The partners in a marriage develop and change and the pregnancy is a period of potentially rapid personality growth for both. It is a fortunate couple who find that the pattern of their expectations, values and fulfilments progresses reciprocally. Biologically the mother experiences greater change and this is mirrored in the expectations that she, her husband and society have of her. An expectant mother publicly proclaims the fact in her changing shape. The expectant father in Victorian tradition was little more than a figure of fun – a superfluous male in a female world. One can only speculate rather gloomily on the effects that this derisive attitude has had on the family. Both men and women probably now have greater personal expectations of the marriage relationship than their grandparents did. (For a further exploration of this thesis the reader is recommended to Ronald Fletcher's *The Family*.)

The expectant father role is at present in process of being defined. The trend is certainly towards a much more active involvement of the father with events during the maternalizatum (see p. 101 this chapter).

It is probably true to say that the father role is easily understood in relation to older children. Babies, by tradition are seen as relating primarily to their mother. It has been found, however, that the development of early attachments may be to more than one person and is sometimes primarily made with the father. Schaffer and Emerson (1964) found that over a quarter of 58 babies they studied selected father as the chosen attachment object.

The midwife's activities, advice and guidance during the pregnancy are likely to affect the attitude of both parents to each other to the pregnancy and therefore to the baby when he arrives. This is perhaps a particularly important factor when we consider the father's position. He may, initially, be unsure of what is expected of him. The development of the expectant father role may turn out to be of great importance in the maintenance of family relationships and therefore in providing a suitable environment for the development of the child's full potentialities. If as we think a midwife should take broad consideration of the family happiness and the infant's long term development into her reckoning, appropriate steps to achieve these objectives have to be taken as early as possible.

The unsupported, unmarried mother usually causes the midwife considerable concern. Unmarried and unsupported are not necessarily the same thing; what matters is whether the mother has a relationship with someone who can make suitable economic provision, help her and generally share the joys and frustrations of caring for the baby. Social security provides for a minimum standard of living so that no woman should be destitute. There is more to life than material survival, however. There is sharing and communication, understanding and learning from a relationship that derives its meaning from the opportunity it gives the participants for personal and social growth.

A woman on her own with a young baby is denied much of this opportunity. To love her baby she needs to experience love herself. Unmarried mothers do not have a monopoly of this deprived emotional life, however. Every marriage does not develop in the way the partners may have originally hoped. They may quarrel, or the marriage can quietly decay for lack of common interests, and an absence of demands and rewards. The pregnant wife of such a marriage may be economically secure but psychologically unsupported. Conversely a woman without a husband may have a good and loving relationship with someone who can provide her with the necessary emotional sustenance. This provision is occasionally made by parents. The risk they run of usurping the maternal role is, however, obvious, particularly if the expectant mother is herself little more than a girl.

So the midwife has a dual concern; one for the material facilities and support that the pregnant woman has available; the other for the affectionate and caring relationships she has. These two factors will enter into consideration if the possibility of abortion is reviewed. Should abortion be unacceptable the question of the baby being adopted may then have to be discussed.

Abortion or adoption may be a solution in some cases. Despite appearances there are probably few truly accidental pregnancies. Some single women plan their family with as much foresight as a well regulated married couple. For some a pregnancy is disastrous, perhaps affecting educational or career prospects, threatening established relationships and upsetting families. For most unsupported mothers the position is neither a disaster, nor the outcome of careful calculation but somewhere between. The midwife has to keep the welfare of both mother and baby in mind. If the mother wants to keep her baby she will need as much support as she can get and it will be worth discussing with her what resources she has – is the baby's father interested? Or will her own family help her? Young women from some immigrant groups can be rejected by their own people and are in a pathetically isolated situation. There is the young woman who has known little of a caring family life herself, who is highly, but unrealistically motivated to have a baby thinking that he will provide her with the loving and belonging experiences of which life has cheated her. Unfortunately such young women rarely have the resources to enable a baby to learn affection from them. Nor do they realise the demands an infant will make. The risk of mother and child eventually separating to create the same problem in the next generation is quite high.

The problem of schoolgirl mothers has increased in recent years. Disturbed adolescent girls are often shy, timid and inhibited and little complained about because they cause no nuisance. The small proportion who do act out the troubles of disordered and conflict-ridden homes at adolescence often do so by sexual misconduct. This may be promiscuous or through the formation of a strong but quite unsuitable relationship. Their indiscriminate search for the affection which they have not experienced at home can make havoc of their young lives.

The situation in the last decade has been changed by a more general acceptance of pre-marital sexual freedom and a relaxation of restrictions on adolescents both concerning their sexual behaviour and the availability of contraceptives. The age of maturity has also been decreasing for some time. Patterns of adolescent sexual behaviour have probably changed since Schofield's study *The Sexual Behaviour of Young People* (1964) but this is to some extent a matter of speculation. It is probably the less well organised girl, with personal and family problems, who is the more likely to become pregnant, however, and to present herself as one of the least able to contend with the demands of unsupported motherhood.

During the antenatal period adoption may be the course decided upon. An adoption is usually arranged through an adoption society, a local authority or, until recently, a 'third party' i.e. their own parents or some other individual.

Whether she decides on abortion, adoption or to keep the baby, the unsupported mother, whatever her age or background needs the best facilities that can be made available.

REFERENCES

Breen, D. (1975) *Birth of a First Child*. London: Tavistock Publications Ltd.
Butler, N. (1969) Perinatal Problems. 2nd Report. *Perinatal Mortality Survey*. Edinburgh: Livingstone.
Donald, Ian. (1972) *Practical Obstetric Problems*. 4th Edn., p. 3. London: Lloyd Luke Medical Books.
Eastham, E., Smith, D., Poole, D., & Neligan, G., (1976) *British Medical Journal*, **1** pp 305-307.
Fletcher, R. (1966) *The Family & Marriage in Britain*. London: Penguin.
Frommer, E.A. (1973) *British Journal of Psychiatry*, **123** No. 573.
Gavron, H. (1966) *The Captive Wife*. London: Penguin.
Hanford, J. (1968) Pregnancy as a state of Conflict. *Psychological Reports*, **22** (3). pp. 1313-1342.
Harlow, H.F. & Harlow, M.K. (1966) Learning to Love. *American Scientist*, **54** pp 244-272.
Horobin, G. & Davis, A. (1977) *Medical Encounters*. London: Croom Helm.
Keeley, K. (1962) Prenatal Experience on Behaviour of offspring of crowded mice. *Science*, **135** p 44.
Kolstad, P. (1957) Therapeutic Abortion. *Acta Obstetrics & Gynaecologica Scandinavia*, **36**. Supplement 6.
Lafitte, F. (1972) *New Society*. **22** No. 532 pp 622-626.
Lovegrove, S. (1976) *Stuck at Home*. London: BBC Publications.
McKenna, J. (1976) Antenatal preparation and epidural anaesthesia. *Midwife, Health Visitor & Community Nurse*, **12** No. 3 pp 78-81.
Masters, W.H. & Johnson, V.E. (1966) *Human Sexual Response*. Boston: Little, Brown.
Mead, M. (1950) *Male & Female*. London: Victor Gollancz.
Menninger, W.C. (1943) The Emotional Factors in Pregnancy. *Menninger Clinic Bulletin*, **7** pp 15-24.
Nilsson, L. (1970) *Acta Psychiatrica Scandinavica*. Supplement 220.

Oakley, A. (1975) The trap of medicalised motherhood. *New Society*. **34** No. 689 pp 639-641.

Pasamanick, B. & Knoblock, H. (1966) Retrospective Studies on the Epidemiology of Reproductive Casualty. *Merrill Palmer Quarterly*, **12** (1), 7.

Peck, E. (1973) *The Baby Trap*. London: Heinrich Hanau Publications.

Prevention & Health: Everybody's Business (1976) DHSS. London: HMSO.

Radio Times (1977) pp 68. 19-25th March. London: BBC Publications.

The Report of the Committee on Child Health Services (1976) *Fit for the Future*. p 115. London: HMSO.

Rosengren, W.R. (1961) Some social psychological aspects of delivery room difficulties. *Journal of Nervous & Mental Diseases*, **132** (6) pp 515-521.

Schaffer, H.R. & Emerson, P.E. (1964) The development of Social attachments in Infancy. *Monographs of the Society for Research into Child Development*, **29** No. 3.

Stott, D.H. (1963) How a Disturbed Pregnancy can Harm the Child. *New Scientist*, **320**.

Vernon, P. (1969) *Intelligence & Cultural Environment*. London: Methuen.

8

Labour

Many women find the final four or six weeks of pregnancy extremely tedious. Their cumbersome size and shape prevents easy movement and they tire easily. Labour is inevitable and the prospect of its commencement is often welcome, despite apprehensions as to what is in store. Preparatory classes in the antenatal period may have provided some factual information as to how the baby will be born, and what can be expected during the course of labour. No one, however, can know how they will feel about the experience. Even women who have already had a child may find they have quite forgotten the details of the event. Preparation for labour in the antenatal period can involve both expectant parents. Most primigravidae will have very little idea about how the labour is likely to begin, when they should come to the hospital, or summon the midwife, and what is likely to happen after labour has begun. This information about the physical aspects of labour is often reassuring to both parents. Fathers who have been hesitating over whether to accompany their wives during labour can often come to a rational decision about the matter, when they have a clearer picture of what it entails, and what might be required of them. The physical and mechanical aspects of labour are well understood by the midwife. There is yet much to be discovered about the psychology of parturition although no one doubts the important part which psychological factors can play.

It is evident that women from different cultural backgrounds behave differently in labour. They respond to cultural expectations and norms. Some expect the experience to be agonising and behave as if it is so; others that giving birth is part of the annual round occasioning a brief respite in the day's work. There are shouts, groans and grunts, or quiet decorum which are broadly characteristic of the culture. The influence of past experience, of expectation, of ideas about childbirth, and about her own body are all likely to affect the behaviour and experience of a woman during labour. 'So childbirth may be experienced according to the phrasing given it by the culture, as an experience which is dangerous and painful, interesting and engrossing, matter of fact and mildly hazardous, or accompanied by enormous supernatural hazards', (Mead 1950).

In the past few years it has become accepted, in most places, that fathers may if they wish, stay with their wives in the labour ward. The modern management of labour has virtually eliminated prolonged labour which was often distressing to the patient and onlookers, and has been a factor facilitating the involvement of husbands. Many fathers to whom we have spoken are delighted to have taken a part in the event and they certainly sound as if their relationships with their children are richer for having seen the very beginning of their life. Some systematic study of fathers in the labour ward is necessary in order to assess the importance of various factors. The experience may have a profound effect on their parenting behaviour and therefore on family life in general. A husband can be a great comfort, simply by being present during the labour. A short play called 'That's my Baby' showed the relationship between husband and wife during the antenatal period and during the labour. They had made up their minds before the labour that it was going to be a *natural* one. The husband took on the important role of protecting his wife from the persistent attempts by the obstetrician to administer drugs, send the husband home, and generally interfere to control the course of events. It was an excellent illustration of the fact that, for obstetricians and midwives, the understanding of physical events of childbirth is often far in advance of the understanding of the psychology of parturition. A recent survey published by the Association for the Improvement of Maternity Services (AIMS) has shown that over 80 per cent of women who have experienced both home and hospital confinements preferred to have their babies at home, (AIMS 1975). At home the mother is surrounded by people and objects with which she is familiar, and she and the baby are central figures in the family drama. The domiciliary midwife has usually had prolonged contact and establishes a close relationship with the mother and family. Lady Micklethwait, President of the National Childbirth Trust wrote 'Our experience, in close contact with parents before and after childbirth, has taught us that good emotional support and encouragement during labour can not only reinforce the effect of any drugs that need to be given for pain relief, but can sometimes mean that this kind of medication is unnecessary' (*The Sunday Times* 1974). The favourable rating of home confinements by those women with the necessary experience to make informed comparison, must surely be derived from the value they attribute to intangible factors. They feel happier with people they know on their own territory, where they are understood and where they are in a web of established relationships. The most ardent advocates of home confinements have never claimed the technical equipment is superior to that of hospital. The easy communication and good relations which characterise a contented family is rarely experienced in hospital. These may be important factors which are in need of special attention by the midwife looking after women in labour in hospital.

In general hospitals it has been found that inhibitions to a free flow of information, and discussion, has a measurable effect on both staff turnover and the speed of patient recovery, (Revans 1964). Learning is essentially a 'feed-back' process, and depends upon seeing the effect of one's own behaviour. Without a flow of information uncertainty increases and with it anxiety. It is the anxiety which affects staff morale and patient recovery. It also increases the subjective assessment of pain.

In midwifery, as in medical practice generally, the patient as a source of ideas and initiative has probably been underrated. This has led inadvertently to a serious undermining of the positive contribution which a woman feels she can make to labour. Kitzinger (1971) reporting on communications received by the National Childbirth Trust from mothers says 'It is intended that the mother shall feel secure and confident but when she asks a question she may well be told "Leave it all to us, you can trust us to decide what is best for you", or even, "What's it got to do with you? You mind your business and we'll mind ours!" ' These responses, and many similar emphasise to an alarming degree the divorce between physiological and psychological understanding. Actually giving birth to the baby becomes somebody else's responsibility. The dilatation of the cervix, position of the fetal head are undoubtedly important concerns. So too, is the significance and meaning a woman is able to attribute to the whole event. Is childbirth simply a matter of the mechanical progress of the baby through the birth canal, or the final exhilarating experience of bringing forth the life which has been nurtured unseen, but felt within, for so many weeks? The significance of that new life for the mother, father, the family can be enhanced by an acknowledgement of the family relationship which have brought it into being, and which will influence its further development. Mothers usually know little of biparietal diameters, and pelvic measurements. What they do know is that they love or hate, are euphoric or depressed, feel the positive motivating force of the contractions or the pain of resisting them. A woman may feel during labour that the baby is, as it has been for the preceding months, an integral part of *her* physically, mentally and spiritually. On the other hand, she may feel it to be a parasite, whose disfiguring dependence is shortly to come to an end. To view the process of labour as simply a mechanical exercise, is to overlook the significance of the feelings of the mother. An exclusive emphasis on the physiology of childbirth can demean the individual mother to a more-or-less efficient reproductive system, and make trivial her important contributions not only to the course of labour, but to events which follow it.

The hurdle concept of pregnancy mentioned in Chapter 8 applies equally to labour. To view it as a temporary aberration from normal, or as a temporary illness, obscures some of the positive developmental processes that are possible. That is not to overlook the abnormal developments which may take place during labour and require urgent intervention. In the last decade techniques which have been found to be effective in the treatment of abnormal obstetric conditions have been increasingly applied to normal ones. The modern management of labour entails the application of three techniques. They are, induction of labour, the administration of oxytocic drugs and epidural analgesia. (Any one of these techniques may be used independently of the other two.) The insertion of prostaglandins in tylose paste into the cervical canal has recently been employed to induce labour without rupturing the membranes. It also precludes the use of intravenous infusion.

The effect of the management of labour on its length and on fetal and maternal mortality and morbidity has been reviewed elsewhere, widely publicised, but is now being reassessed.

The effect of the process on the mothers self-concept and on her mothering role has so far not been investigated. Further evaluation of its effects on the baby are also needed although some studies are already available (see Ch. 4). The very development of management techniques has arisen from, and expedited the improvement of, diagnosis of abnormality.

It is an everyday observation, reinforced by more precise data from experimental studies in social psychology, that the individual is susceptible to pressures to conformity. (Asch 1956 and Sherif 1935). It is also clear that some people are more influential in exerting pressure on others. Numerical strength is important, as is high status and success, indeed the terms are almost synonymous with influence.

The medical profession have for many decades enjoyed high status and an influential position in the community. Within the hospital setting they also have numerical strength. The likelihood is, therefore, that if a condition is defined in medical circles as abnormal it stands a good chance of being accepted as such. Obstetrics in the last decade has become extensively abnormalised and being in labour now not only necessitates going to hospital, but in many cases having a special nurse in constant attendance, (O'Driscoll 1975) a state of affairs usually associated with serious illness. It is likely that a proportion of normal women with normal pregnancies succumb to expectations. We suggest here the process by which this may occur. By defining labour as a medical event requiring hospital treatment, and highly skilled surveillance, the general level of anxiety about it may be raised. There is evidence that pre-natal attitudes and anxieties have an effect on the length of labour and the incidence of complications. (Engström *et al.* 1964, Davids and Devaultz 1962, Zemlick and Watson 1953.) Crawford (1969) has suggested the mechanism by which fears and anxieties can affect the process of labour. As a result of anxiety adrenaline is secreted into the bloodstream, and this restricts the blood supply to, and contractions of, the uterus. Hawkins (1974) says 'The main effect of adrenaline on the pregnant human uterus is to depress both intensity and frequency of contractions. . . The action is accompanied by tachycardia and systolic hypertension and the utero placental circulation may be affected in an unpredictable manner with the production of fetal distress.' Crawford (1969) found that women who showed overt signs of anxiety at the onset of labour (expressed fear, high pulse rate, etc.) were more likely to develop problems related to uterine dysfunction and their infants to develop hypoxia. Uterine inertia is one of the problems which the active management of labour is designed to ameliorate however, O'Driscoll (1975) notes 'Active management ensures efficient uterine action'. The very prospect for some women of being actively managed however may interfere with the normal sequence of endocrine activity which leads to uterine efficiency. Hypertonic contractions do not always become more efficient even with the use of syntocinon and the possibility that psychological and biochemical events are counteracting each other deserves further exploration.

In so far as modern obstetrics increases anxieties it may have exacerbated the very condition that it seeks to ameliorate. A woman's admission to hospital and her loss of autonomy at the onset of labour invest the experience with a dimension of apprehension which through the consequent endocrine activity, depresses uterine function and increases the liklihood of a delay in labour and fetal distress. This in turn requires further intervention.

Recent debate in both public and medical press has expressed concern about both the short and long term effects of the active management of labour on mothers, their children and their families. As any midwife who has been in practice for ten years will know only too well it has also greatly affected her work and the midwife's role in society.

Induction of labour in England in 1965 was estimated to have been performed in 15 per cent of deliveries and this rose to 31.5 per cent in 1972 and 37.2 per cent in 1973. Provisional data for 1974 showed an incidence of 40.7 per cent (On the State of the Public Health for the year 1975. HMSO 1976). Rates of induction vary from one hospital to another. A multidisciplinary group for the Department of Health & Social Security visited eight hospitals in 1975 to discuss aspects of induction with hospital staff, general practitioners and patients. 'The group found no cause for concern in the current use of induction techniques. . . The impression was that a genuine attempt was being made . . . to offer an improved service to women in childbirth. . . In some cases there did appear to be a failure of communication between staff and their patients. . . It was felt that many of the complaints about induction made by women reflected a deeper underlying dissatisfaction with the extent to which their emotional and psychological needs are being catered for in childbirth', (DHSS Annual Report 1975).

Amniotomy has to be followed by uterine stimulation if contractions do not ensue within a fairly short time. This process involves the midwife in close monitoring of both fetal and maternal conditions because the effects on mother and fetus of the artificially increased strength of contractions is not always predictable. Where epidural analgesia is administered the need for constant surveillance is increased as the mother is unaware of the strength of her uterine activity and the risk of hypotension is ever present.

It has been claimed that one of the advantages of the induction and acceleration of labour is that 'it has created a situation where every woman in labour has a personal nurse... This personal contact provides invaluable support for morale and it also provides an opportunity for student nurses' (sic) 'and doctors to gain an insight into the human element of labour which they previously lacked', (O'Driscoll 1975).

It has always been a requirement of the Central Midwives Board however, that no woman is left alone from the beginning of the second stage of labour until the end of the third stage (CMB 1962) and many have been attended throughout the first stage as well. The midwife, monitoring an actively managed labour, may feel that mechanical knowledge and ability is more relevant than human insight.

It is usually a pupil midwife or obstetric nurse who is required to stay with a woman during the course of a managed labour. She may be both young and inexperienced, obstetrically and generally and may be hard pressed to sustain either her patient or herself with relevant comfort and solace. For two people to have to maintain a relationship while segregated in a separate room for several hours, may be an entertaining and satisfying experience if they like each other. If they do not, or if there is some cause for embarrassment, it may be a great trial. The plight of a distraught pupil who acted as the special nurse for a patient with an intrauterine death for several hours, demands sympathy. It was not clear to her whether the patient was aware that her baby had died. Probably they dared not mention the topic foremost in their minds. Several hours at what is often a monotonous and repetitive task can be very dispiriting. Human beings are extremely bad at maintaining alert attentiveness in conditions of monotony (Mackworth 1950). Any member of staff should have the option of being relieved of such a duty after an hour or at most two.

This may seem to be contradicting our view of the midwife giving continuity of care. It would be very satisfactory if the midwife who had supervised the patient's antenatal care and education, and had come to know her well could be with her throughout her labour. The demands on trained staff however would be excessive, and it seems inevitable that the 'continuity role' must be more supervisory in the first stage, and allow staff in training to carry out this essential job of monitoring of blood pressure, fetal and maternal pulse and so on.

Let us consider the sequence of events during labour and the supportive skills the midwife can bring to them. Labour may begin spontaneously and the first stage may be well advanced before patient and midwife meet. If the patient has attended antenatal classes she and her husband may have decided beforehand whether he is going to stay for the birth of the baby, and they will have some information as to the likely course of events. Patients who have not attended antenatal preparatory classes may need some information at this stage, and both parents need some opportunity for discussion to decide whether the husband is to be present. The patient's fullest cooperation in the birth process is to be encouraged, and she and her husband need to decide whether his presence will help. Husbands in the labour ward have been encouraged in many hospitals, and allowed with varying degrees of resistance in some others.

A considerable proportion of patients are admitted to hospital before labour starts spontaneously, with a view to induction. The unseemly position of lithotomy is unlikely to be reassuring, and patients need a proper explanation of the purpose of an amniotomy. A woman in a position appropriate for an artificial rupture of membranes is unlikely to be sufficiently relaxed to take in all that is said to her at the time by way of explanation. The midwife may do much to encourage her morale, not only by answering questions and providing information, but by assuring her that someone will always be close by, preferably before the procedure is carried out. Ideally the person in constant contact and attendance should be known to the patient. If the important 'continuity role' has been developed during the antenatal period the confidence of the patient is likely to be greatly enhanced. The knowledge that she is being cared for by someone who is aware of her development during the pregnancy will be reassuring. It is to the midwife that women must look to counteract the depersonalisation which accompanies much of modern obstetrics. To provide good continuity of care the midwife needs to know something of the patient's hopes and fears, to be available not only to give information, but to listen. Confidences are only entrusted to those who are known and respected.

The progress of labour may be normal and natural and the patient free to walk around until late first or second stage of labour. When the labour is induced, accelerated, and monitored, movement is often restricted by the infusion and cardiotocograph. Some women in antenatal classes express their apprehension at the idea of being attached to machinery and being unable to get off the bed. There is a number of possible reasons for this. The control of bowel and bladder

Figure 8.1a & b Progress of patient can be checked on monitoring apparatus rather than by personal examination.

movement is very deeply ingrained by early training, as is a strong reticence about their activity. Complaints about not being able to get up to go to the lavatory must be one of the most common in all hospital patients. The return to infancy implied by soiling, or dependence on someone else to deal with these primitive needs, is a trauma not to be lightly dismissed. In addition many women in normal labour find walking about of some comfort. Physiologically it is a better position for facilitating childbirth than being flat on a bed.

Having to keep still on a bed emphasises the sickness or dependence role, while the monitoring apparatus may depersonalise the experience. Attention is divided between the patient on the bed and the machinery at her side (Figs. 8.1a & b). Her progress may be checked less by how she feels, more by the movements on the dial. Close attention to the paper record can provide the obstetrician with the information he needs. This can be acquired without a word to, or an examination of, the patient. It has been known that the recording apparatus was housed in a separate room from the patient so she could be monitored but left alone. This arrangement has now been abandoned, so far as we know.

Some patients express great satisfaction with hospital delivery. Women who have had difficult or very painful deliveries before may be reassured by the quality of technical achievement manifest in a modern labour ward. There may be a number of reasons why they have come to distrust human frailty – including their own. For others the mechanisation of a human experience is objectionable and alienating. The labour ward with its monitoring apparatus, stainless steel and impersonal purity is completely at odds with the homely nest that has been made for the baby in the preceeding weeks (Fig. 8.2). The home is marked by symbols of personal taste and individuality which gives it meaning. The hospital ward has a small area which can be given some personal meaning by photographs on the locker and the paraphernalia of interests and hobbies. The labour ward is purified of every personal symbol, with the permissable exception of a woman's wedding ring.

The midwife may be able to provide good help and support by recognising and responding to the important individual traits and motivations be they attractive or otherwise. Not all women are delighted at the prospect of producing a baby. Some are fearful, resentful, faced with the inevitability of labour and delivery. Very few women openly express hostility to the fetus about to be born, and negative statements about any aspect of having a baby are rarely heard

Figure 8.2. Technical apparatus of labour ward.

in a maternity hospital: yet they must exist. Criticisms of the baby who is the wrong sex are perhaps an exception to this.

There are certainly strong social restrictions to the voicing of criticism. Dana Breen (1975) in her study of women having their first baby suggests that 'the discrepancy between what the woman experiences and what she is told she should be experiencing' can be a factor contributing to post natal depression. Perhaps most women are made to feel that they should be grateful (for all that is done for them) and joyful (with their new baby). What they may feel is resentment and anger (at not being able to do things their own way) and bitter or disappointed (at the birth and their new baby). Post-natal depression is an important problem which is discussed further in the next chapter. It might be to great advantage if the midwife can tolerate, or perhaps even facilitate, the expression of adverse feelings of a woman in labour. What many women fear is that such feelings are unusual, abnormal, and frightening. It cannot be urged too frequently that affection for a baby is largely learned and that no great alarm should arise over the expression of antipathetic feelings during labour, or even on first seeing the baby.

A patient who is immobile because she is attached to apparatus is bound to feel passive rather than active. Her movements, behaviour, progress in labour, her bodily sensations are constrained or initiated at the behest of someone else. She is passively expected to react to management by others, to follow instructions rather than determine the course of events for herself. This becomes more markedly the case for patients who have epidural analgesia. An increase in epidurals seems to be associated with an increase in instrumental delivery. The enormous motive power from within is reduced to a less efficient level. One woman we know had all her four healthy children at home. On every occasion she refused to call the midwife until the very last moment because 'I didn't want anyone to come and fiddle about with me'. Dana Breen (1975) found that the women 'who went through the experience of having a child with least difficulties, where those women who were able to feel themselves to be active, not only after the birth of the baby but also during pregnancy. Such a sense of initiation and activity is one which has often been denied women in our culture.' (Breen 1975). It is denied too to a large number of women who are managed during their labour. The midwife does need to use considerable tact and skill to help a woman in normal labour to retain her initiative and active integrity, and to restrain others with a more active approach to the problem.

Discussion of pain relief is done in some antenatal classes; but not all women attend these. There is often some need therefore to expand on the matter during labour. A few women attend relaxation classes and so successfully apply what they have learned that analgesics are not needed. There are rather few women who manage this. Some apply themselves diligently to exercises and breathing and go to pieces when the going gets rather rougher than they anticipated. They may feel ashamed at having lost control or frightened because they believe something abnormal is occurring. Others are ready to consider analgesics if necessary but want to know what risks to themselves and the baby are associated with each method. The acceleration of labour by oxytocic drugs of course makes contractions suddenly become stronger, and therefore women in accelerated labour are likely to require more pain relief. There is evidence that the analgesic given to the mother during labour does affect the infant. By making him drowsy and unresponsive the early mother – baby relationship may be more difficult to establish. Babies whose mothers have had barbiturates or pethidine suck with less vigour and perhaps because of that gain weight less well. They habituate more slowly, are more difficult to console and have more interuptions in their feeding, (Brazelton 1973, Richards & Bernal 1973). Whether there are any long term consequences is not yet clear.

The subjective experience of pain has no direct relationship to the extent of physical trauma. There is much evidence that the experience of pain is affected by previous experiences and how well they are remembered, by the understanding we have of the cause of the pain and its consequences. Different cultures accord different kinds of significance to pain and these evaluations are learned during growing up. Animals reared in conditions where they experienced no hurtful stimuli appeared lacking in a proper appreciation of pain when they were grown up. They made no effort to get away from a flame, showed little evidence of pain when pricked, (Thompson & Melzack 1956).

Sportsmen often sustain serious injury on the playing field and fail to notice it till the game is over. Soldiers in combat have been oblivious to extensive trauma. Any situation that attracts attention away from the source of the pain tends to reduce the experience of it. Hypnosis works on this basis. Hypnosis is a trance like state in which the subject's attention is focused intensely on the hypnotist while attention to other stimili is markedly diminished. A few people are sufficiently susceptible to undergo surgery without anaesthesia. For some others hypnosis can reduce the amount of analgesic required.

Emotional support has already been referred to as effective in reducing pain (see p. 116). Attention is diverted from the source of the pain and the personal contact reduces fear. Anyone who has suffered prolonged pain regards it as an evil, and harmful in itself.

Yet the positive aspects of pain as a biological warning system are well recognised. Any experienced midwife knows the element of pain relief there is in the confidence a patient has in her. This effective confidence is not established quickly, and the need for it gives added point to our proposition that the effective midwife needs to maintain a continuity role with the patient.

The husband in the labour ward if he is suitably motivated and informed may well be able to provide vital confidence and support.

Henneborn and Cogan (1975) have studied the effects of husbands at the delivery, (Fig. 8.3). They found that the presence of husbands (who had attended antenatal classes) had a positive effect on their wives' reported feelings of pain, and there was a decreased use of medication. For the hospital delivery the husband too is on strange territory, and he will be much less able to help his wife if his own position is ambiguous by his being made to feel unwelcome. Some people have argued that husbands might lay claim to the right to be in the labour ward. If he is there, the wise midwife can make full use of his consoling potential by assuring him of a welcome, making it clear to him how he can help and what he can do. If he has a clearly defined role he is likely to live up to it. Only when he does not know what is expected of him, is he likely to get in the way, or faint, as some of his critics have claimed! This might well be a mismanagement of a

Figure 8.3. Husband participating in the labour ward.

valuable resource. He also needs help and considerate support as it is often as difficult to watch suffering as to experience it.

Episiotomy and instrumental delivery have increased together with the increase in the control of labour. Both of these activities, like amniotomy and administration of oxytocic drugs, have as their rationale, the acceleration of delivery. An increase in instrumental delivery may be associated upon the increase in the use of epidural analgesic often needed because of the increased strength of contractions in accelerated labour. Epidural analgesia, as well as deadening the painful experience of uterine contractions reduces or removes the urgency for women to make expulsive effort.

The advantages and disadvantages of these practices have been hotly debated by a variety of interested groups. Obstetricians, paediatricians, midwives, psychologists, women's movements, patients' associations, especially those which concern themselves with the services available to pregnant and parturient women, have all expressed their views. The debate is basically an ideological one. Those who favour control and acceleration argue that a proportion of women, especially those having first babies, are going to have abnormal labours and it is impossible to predict in advance those who are at risk. Caution therefore demands that all patients to be treated as high risk. As it is during the labour and delivery that emergencies arise, the more speedily mother and baby are separated under conditions of maximum surveillance, the better. Those who take the opposite view regard childbirth as a natural phenomenon in which a myriad of factors orchestrate in a finely balanced, but as yet poorly understood way. Proponents of this view believe that a spontaneous delivery by a healthy, self-confident, and reasonably happy woman cannot be improved upon, and that the job of the maternity services is to enhance the woman's health, self-confidence and happiness. This they claim can best be achieved by encouraging her autonomy, providing moral support and eschewing all meddling (Kloosterman 1975).

There has been, of course, a dramatic improvement in maternal and perinatal mortality rates but it would be a mistake to attribute this necessarily to interventionist policies of current obstetrics in the United Kingdom. In Holland where about 50 per cent of babies are born at home the mortality rates are even lower. Perinatal and infant mortality rates are sensitive indicators of social conditions. The midwife in the labour ward has, however, to work within the constraints of the immediate situation, where these wider considerations may seem remote. Patients who are drowsy through medication are not necessarily unaware of what is said or done around them, nor are their husbands. They sometimes cannot, often do not, make it plain that they can both see and hear. It is unlikely to do the patient a service to openly comment upon episiotomy or haemorrhage or to display to view implements for instrumental delivery. Not only is she likely to be frightened unnecessarily but any misunderstanding can undermine her confidence in the staff, which may subsequently have serious consequences.

Some women experience an instrumental delivery as a great disappointment. They feel they have been cheated of the chance of achievement. In 1974 38.3 per cent of women delivered at Queen Charlotte's Hospital had instrumental deliveries (including 9.2 per cent Caesarian sections), (Craft 1976). This proportion probably reflects disappointments on the part of the midwife and pupil midwives as well, for both they and the mother have effectively lost command of the situation.

Probably the most rewarding experience for both parents and midwife is the occasion when the mother retains sufficient consciousness and control to actively participate in and watch the birth of the baby. This can be an ecstatic experience. Aidan McFarlane (1977) has recorded the conversations between parents, baby and staff at and immediately following normal deliveries. Against the background of realism with crying baby, metallic instruments, blood and dirty linen they speak a profound pleasure. The baby is inspected minutely, discussed and put in a relationship to various members of the family. 'Got my nose and ears', 'big feet', 'look at his hair', 'to be known as Kirsty', 'you're not a Cameron at all', 'She's lovely. I thought she'd be all mauve and crinkly' 'Well it will suit your Mum won't it?' The opportunity for the mother and father to look at and handle the baby within seconds of his birth gives great pleasure (Fig. 8.4). They can assure themselves of his good health and take pride in their achievement, and have their first conversation with the new member of the family. Many mothers have complained that their babies are taken away after the birth and they may not see them again for several hours. If the mother was not conscious for the delivery she may spend hours worrying about his very existence.

The unsupported mother at the antenatal clinic has been discussed. When she is in labour she is likely to need special care and attention from the midwife. The schoolgirl mother is a subject of particular concern. Scarcely out of childhood herself she may be the focal point of many problems. Not infrequently from a disrupted family she may be blamed, abused or ignored by her upset parents on account of the pregnancy. She may be advised, cajoled or bullied by a cacophony of voices not necessarily with her or the baby's welfare as priorities. Some young pregnant girls can easily be overwhelmed by their mothers who plan to take over the baby and treat him as their own. The grafting of

Figure 8.4. Mother and father handling baby immediately after birth.

the new baby on to the end of an established family may be satisfactory where it is done with affection tact and consideration for the baby and the true mother. There are families however where this has set the scene for disasterous confusion of relationships. The child is often brought up believing his mother to be his sister, his uncle to be his brother, his grandmother his mother and so on. The discovery of the truth of these relationships can be disruptively distressing. The realignment of such close relationships implies a major realignment of the self, and may herald the onset of psychotic behaviour (Gibbens 1963).

A woman who has decided during the pregnancy that the baby is to be adopted will also, it is hoped, have had the opportunity of discussing the implications of this decision (see p. 112-4). Mothers who are separated from their babies involuntarily or whose babies die, suffer anxiety, depression or grief. A voluntary giving away of the baby involves more personal responsibility and possibly a stronger feeling of guilt. Children sometimes go to inordinate lengths to try to find their lost parents. They feel that they are incomplete unless they can find the people who gave them their beginning. Without this knowledge they are unable to answer the question 'Who am I?' to their satisfaction. It is now legally possible and permissible for adopted children to trace their biological parents. This is likely to have a considerable impact on attitudes to adoption as the ill begotten child may resurface after eighteen years.

When the baby is born there is the question of whether the mother should see, or hold her baby. The longer mother and baby are in contact the greater the wrench of separation when it comes. Some women decide firmly not to see the baby at all, and keep to their plan. Some make the decision and change their minds at the birth. Some never make any hard and fast decision and, of course, some who have planned adoption all through the pregnancy change their minds after the birth.

Folklore and myth abound with stories of revenge exacted, peace restored, old scores settled by the emergence in adulthood of children abandoned, given away or believed dead. The recurrence of such themes shows how feelings of guilt, hope or grief remain unresolved and emerge in symbolic form in such stories as Oedipus Rex, The Winter's Tale, Snowwhite and many others. The child who is the focus of suspicion, embarrassment or threat may be put out of sight but not out of mind. We have been unable to find any systematic study of women who have had their babies adopted. The recent change in the law relating to adopted children adds another variable to be taken into account when coming to a decision.

Mothers used to be obliged to look after their babies for six weeks before placing them for adoption and the overt purpose was to give them time to make a considered decision. Another six weeks follows before the court order can be made. Many undoubtedly became attached to their babies in that time and either changed their minds or suffered considerably at the parting. It seemed to many people kinder to let a woman avoid becoming really fond of her baby by not having contact. How far this new legislation will affect decisions at birth remains to be seen. A midwife who inevitably becomes involved in discussion and decisions on the issue should be aware of the complex psycho-social issues involved.

We hear a lot about the need to support the family against all the insidious pressures that are suspected of weakening it. What goes on during labour and delivery may have effects on the way the mother sees herself – active or passive – directed or autonomous – in control or the victim of circumstances. The midwife has a clear and influential role to play, in helping the mother to adapt effectively and to sustain a positive vigorous attitude to herself, her baby and her family.

REFERENCES

Asch, S.E. (1956) Studies of independence and submission to group pressure. *Psychological Monographs,* **70**. No. 416.

Association for the Improvement of the Maternity Services. (1975) *Quarterly Newsletter,* March. p. 7.

Brazelton, T.B. (1973) Effect of prenatal drugs on the behaviour of the neonate. *American Journal of Psychiatry,* **126**. pp 1261-1266.

Breen, Dana. (1975) *Birth of a First Child.* London: Tavistock Publications.

CMB Handbook 25th Edition **1962** p. 59.

Craft, Ian. (1976) Induction of Labour. *Midwife, Health Visitor & Community Nurse,* **12**. pp 42-44.

Crawford, Mary I. (1969) Psychological & Behavioural Clues to Disturbances in Childbirth. Columbia University Dissertation. Available in the UK in *Dissertation Abstracts,* **29** (7-B) p. 2504.

Davids, A. & Devault, S. (1962) Maternal Anxiety during Pregnancy and Childbirth Abnormalities. *Psychosomatic Medicine,* **24** 5 pp 464-470.

Annual Report of the Chief Medical Officer for 1975 (1976) DHSS. London: HMSO.

Engstrom, L., Afgeiterstam, G., Holmberg, N.G. & Uhrus, K. (1964) A prospective study of the relationship between psycho-social factors and the course of pregnancy and delivery. *Journal of Psychosomatic Research,* **8**. pp 151-155.

Gibbens, T.C.N. (1963) *Psychiatric Studies of Borstal Lads.* Oxford: O.U.P.

Hawkins, D.F. (1974) The pharmacology of the pregnant human uterus. In *Obstetric Therapeutics,* Ed. Hawkins, D.F. p. 31. London: Balliere.

Henneborn, W.J. & Cogan, R. (1975) The effect of husband participation on reported pain and the probability of medication during labour and birth. *Journal of Psychosomatic Research, 1i.* pp 215-222.

Kitzinger, Sheila. (1971) Woman on the Delivery Table. In *Woman on Woman.* Ed. Laing, Margaret. London: Sidgwick & Jackson.

Kloosterman, G.J. (1975) Obstetrics in the Netherlands – a survival or a challenge? (Paper presented to the Meeting on Problems in Obstetrics organised by the Medical Information Unit of Spastics' Society at Tunbridge Wells.)

McFarlane, Aidan. (1977) *Psychology of Childbirth.* London: Fontana Open Books.

Mackworth, N.H. (1950) Researches in the Measurement of Human Performance. *M.R.C. Special Report Series.* No. **268**. London: HMSO.

Mead, Margaret. (1950) *Male and Female.* London: Victor Gollanz.

O'Driscoll, Kieran. (1975) Active Management of Labour. *Midwife, Health Visitor & Community Nurse,* **11**. pp 146-148.

Revans, R.W. (1964) Standards for morale: cause and effect in hospitals. Oxford: Oxford University Press for the Nuffield Provincial Hospital Trust.

Richards, M.P.M. & Bernal, J.F. (1972) An observational study of mother-infant interaction. In *Ethological Studies of Child Behaviour*. Ed. Burton-Jones, N. London: Cambridge University Press.

Sherif, M. (1935) A Study of some Social Factors in Perception. *Archives of Psychology*, **27**. No. 187. pp 5, 17, 34, 41.

Thompson, W.R. & Melzack, R. (1956) Early Environment. *Scientific American*, **194**. pp 38-42.

Zemlick, M.J. & Watson, D. (1953) Maternal attitudes of acceptance and rejection during and after pregnancy. *American Journal of Orthopsychiatry*, **23**. pp 570-584.

9

Post-natal events

In the chapter on Neonatal abilities we were concerned in the main with the baby's needs and activities. These can only take shape and acquire significance in the way they interact with other people – in particular the mother. She too has needs and feelings and may be elated or depressed, contented or agitated, secure or fearful.

In this country mothers are often given their babies to look at, hold, perhaps to put to the breast, when they are born (Fig. 9.1). The infant is usually wrapped in a sheet and this precludes a close examination of him by his mother. By the time mother meets her baby again, he is usually cleanly dressed in shirt and napkin, and warmly tucked under blankets.

Figure 9.1. Newly born baby at mother's breast.

Two American pediatricians have filmed a number of mothers with their new babies in their first prolonged contact with them. An overhead heated canopy kept the babies warm so they could be left naked. On analysing the film material, it was found that when mothers are left alone to look at, and examine their naked baby they all follow a similar pattern of behaviour. They touch hands and feet first with their finger tips, and then after several minutes touch his whole body with the palms of the hands. Attempts to get the baby to open his eyes are common and in order to do this they generally support his whole body in an en-face position – that is so that they are face to face, and speak to him. The researchers Klaus and Kennell (1970) have suggested that this sequence of behaviour may be important in establishing early ties of affection between mother and child.

Mothers have complained bitterly that their babies are sometimes whisked away from them after birth, before they have had time to get acquainted. Their need to explore and to get to know their baby is frustrated. Some mothers go home from hospital having never seen their baby naked. A survey done by the Royal College of Midwives (1966) showed that the most common fear of pregnant women is that they will have an abnormal baby. A close inspection has the practical aim of reassurance on this matter; but there is perhaps a less obvious, but very important motivation of making the first steps in an acquaintance process.

About 10 per cent of babies now spend some part of the first days of their life in special or intensive care units. In some hospitals parents are strongly encouraged to visit their babies in the nursery. Despite encouragement there are difficulties for mothers in maintaining contact. Harper *et al.*, (1976) have found that high levels of contact with babies in special care units, are correlated with high anxiety. Having a very small or ill baby is a worrying event; the special care unit in itself is frightening for many parents (Figs. 9.2a & b). The appearance of the baby is usually very far from the ideal which the mother has been imagining during the months of pregnancy. Not only may her baby's appearance seem bizarre, but his behaviour is quite different from that of a normal baby.

At the birth of a normal healthy baby mothers get very exicted when their babies open their eyes. Eye to eye contact has great significance in all social relations. We signal an interest by looking at another person, pay attention to what they are saying by watching their face, and lovers gaze into each others eyes (Fig. 9.3). Traditionally the eyes are the

Figure 9.2a & b The need to put babies in special care units can give mothers much anxiety.

windows of the soul. Small or ill babies open their eyes very little, and it is difficult if not impossible, for their mothers to maintain eye contact with them (Fig. 9.4). In addition, if they cannot handle them they are unable to hold them in an *en face* position.

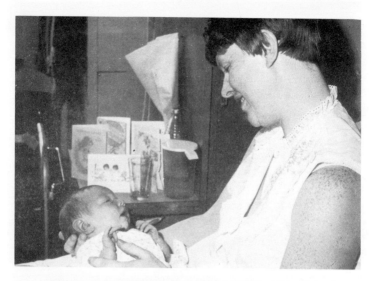

Figure 9.3. Eye to eye contact between mother and baby.

Figure 9.4. Absence of eye contact with an ill baby.

Bowlby (1969) has suggested that the baby's cry acts to elicit caring and nurturant response in the mother. This sort of behaviour may be less well developed in the mother of a baby whose cry is feeble or infrequent. Moss (1967) has found that mothers pick up their boy babies in the first three months of life more often than they do girls, and that boys cry more often.

Despite parental anxiety provoked by the birth of a small or ill baby Harper (1976), in the study already mentioned, found that, even when the baby died, 90 per cent of parents would have opposed any restriction of contact. That is, their motivation to be with their baby is stronger than their motivation to run away from the frightening situation.

Professional staff quickly become familiarised with the apparatus of the special care unit (Fig. 9.5). It can be very chilling to a new mother, who is at the same time having to contend with some rapid hormonal changes within, the worry of a very ill baby, and questioning relatives without. Most special care units are inhumanly quiet, clinically hygenic, and very uncomfortable. The hard metal seats which constitute the furnishings of the units which we know, are hardly designed to encourage prolonged visiting by a mother with perineal stitches.

The midwife and special care unit nurse have an important job in encouraging the mother to take as much part as she is able, in the care

Figure 9.5. Professional staff operating within a special care unit with facility.

of her baby. The necessary physical care requires a high level of technical competence which most mothers do not have, and there are, therefore problems about role relationships between mother and nurse. A mother could be encouraged to take an increasing part in helping with the baby's care. Some mothers are initially very frightened to even go near their children, especially those in incubators. A frightened mother who is not supported is likely to visit the nursery less and less. Evidence shows that even with encouragement, the contact between parents and their babies in incubators, is very much less than that between normal babies and their mothers in hospitals (Prince, Firlej & Harvey – in press). In our experience this can result in the nursing staff becoming critical of the mother and becoming protective and concerned for the baby. By the time the infant is well enough to be transferred to parental care the mother's maternal behaviour may have been seriously disrupted. She may by that time have *got the message* that she is an incompetent mother who cannot manage. The baby who starts life in a special care unit has a somewhat increased risk of being injured by his parents than other healthy children in the same family (Lynch 1975).

Difficulties of pregnancy and delivery which are likely to lead to a baby going to a special or intensive care unit, are more common in the lower socio-economic groups. It is in these socially less favoured families that physically aggressive behaviour is more commonly found. The baby's sojourn in a special care unit is only one of numerous factors which can militate against a good relationship between mother and child. It is therefore of vital importance that the mother become progressively involved with her baby during his stay in the unit.

For the apprehensive mother the rituals associated with entry to a special care unit are daunting (Fig. 9.6). The midwife can be reassuring by accompanying the mother for as long as is necessary, helping her with the procedures for the prevention of infection, and staying with her when she goes to her baby, and encouraging appropriate contact. The father's role is important too. The care of a sick baby is made easier if both parents are involved and there is evidence that support and concern of the father is an important factor in ameliorating a mother's difficulties with her new baby (Blake, Stewart and Turcan 1975). To witness the passing of a nasal tube on her baby, or to see him have an injection may be very upsetting to a mother. These are procedures which it may be tactful to do in the mother's absence. If

Figure 9.6. Washing hands is just one of the rituals for the mother involved with the special care of her baby.

they are done when she is present careful explanation should be made beforehand.

The majority of babies born are normal and healthy and some of their mothers are grateful in the first day or two after delivery to be assured of prolonged rest, and are therefore quite pleased if their baby is in a separate nursery at night. Others would prefer to have their babies either in the cot, or in bed with them. One of the advantages of small wards or cubicles is that mothers can have more choice in this matter. It is possible to put three or four mothers who want their babies with them all the time in the same ward. Their infants' sleeping habits will not then inconvenience any mother who wants to sleep soundly all night.

It will be clear from the preceding chapters that many changes take place in the mother after delivery, which enable her to synchronise her activity with that of the baby. In some women the process takes longer than in others. Mothers of first babies have usually had little or no experience of any baby, and the meaning of his signals, how to console, speak to and handle him, all have to be learned. The ease with which this learning is acquired, probably has little to do with intelligence or intellectual achievement. In some respects the highly educated mother may be initially at a disadvantage. Her educational achievements may have required her to develop an analytic style of thinking which can inhibit spontaneous, emotionally responsive, behaviour. It may be a mistake to believe that midwives and pediatricians, for example, with their own first babies, are going to feel good about themselves or their offspring. They may *know* what should be done in an intellectual sense, but experience a delay in the development of the spontaneous inner-sprung need to handle, talk to, be with their baby, which they could describe as loving him. It is rather like learning to ride a bicycle. It is a help to understand about gravity and the principles of balance, but the automatic reactions necessary for smoothly integrated behaviour require additional learning, which comes with practice, and someone who analyses her cycle riding activity minutely may take longer to learn. A midwife should be cautious of assuming that a mother who *knows about* babies can manage her own straight away. She may be the very person who needs more, rather than less, support. She is likely to have more factual information to worry about. 'Is the baby's cord alright . . . has he passed urine . . . are his respirations satisfactory and his airway clear?' The less well informed mother will take it for granted that all the basic functions of her infant are in satisfactory order so she can relax more readily to enjoy his company. In addition, the well informed mother may be reticent in asking advice if she knows the staff expect her to be competent. A midwife, highly regarded by her colleagues professionally, was visited by one of them after she had had her own baby. She looked tired and drawn and the baby was irritable and was said to be losing weight. In the kitchen were twelve assorted tins of milk food! When something goes awry with a highly practised skill, the whole well organised sequence of behaviour can crumble. Panic ensues, and the position can get completely out of control.

Changes in personality and maternal feeling are apparent during the pregnancy. For many women however it is after delivery, when the child they have been waiting for, and thinking about, becomes a reality, that changes in feeling and in role become more noticeable.

Dana Breen (1975) found in the women with first babies whom she studied that 60 per cent of them thought they had changed since the pregnancy began. Some of the others thought they had changed during the pregnancy, but had reverted to their former selves post natally. When asked what the most significant aspect of the whole experience of child bearing had been, the most frequently mentioned time was the post partum period, and relating to the baby. The second most common was the actual birth. This points to childbirth and the postnatal period as being perhaps the critically important time for personality growth and role modification. The relationship of mother to baby inevitably has an effect on her relationship with her husband, as well as other less centrally placed people (for example the baby's maternal grandmother). Preparatory steps taken in the antenatal period may have provided a *run-in* to the necessary changes but can never completely anticipate them. It is likely that inadequate preparation will mean that some rather abrupt changes will take place at, or fairly soon after, the birth.

Most midwives will be familiar with the mild depressive state which afflicts a number of mothers about the third or fourth day after delivery. It is often assumed that *the blues* are normal. In the sense that they occur in a large number of mothers this is undoubtedly true. Yalom *et al.,* (1968) for example found that two-thirds of a group of mothers they studied cried for trivial reasons, realising this was for them unusual. The common cold is, in this sense normal, but nevertheless considerable effort is expended, not only in ameliorating its symptoms, but finding its cause. Little attention is paid to finding the cause of mild postnatal depression, although a number of untested assumptions have been put forward.

Endocrine changes are considerable and affect emotional reactions. It is also on about the third or fourth day that the sudden drop in oestrogen, which accompanies sudden filling of the breasts, is acutely felt. This event may have a more dramatic, though temporary effect on a woman's self-image, than is generally conceded. The breast has become the focus of eroticised sexual interest. Changes in contour and the discomfort of engorged breasts, may arouse considerable sexual as well as maternal anxieties. Women who plan to breast feed often experience two or three days of tearful frustration when the baby finds it difficult to maintain suction. Bottle feeding mothers are increasingly exposed to persuasion to change their minds, and some readily concede that breast feeding is better for their baby. Breast engorgement may, in these circumstances, serve to highlight for them the dissonance between their social-sexual self and their maternal-self.

Within a few days of delivery the majority of women feel physically healthy, and the immediate reason for their being in hospital has passed. Associated with the immediate recovery from delivery may be homesickness and mild depression at being on foreign territory. Women often find they quarrel with one another over small things from about the fourth day. As soon as is possible, siblings should be encouraged to visit (Figs. 9.7a & b). The early transfer of mother and baby home is likely to have a beneficial effect on the family. Other siblings will not be separated from their mother for so long, and the problems that so often follow for the child who is separated from his mother, need not be added to the possibly unavoidable one of jealousy in a youngster who feels himself displaced. Early discharge is sometimes resisted as being too fatiguing for the mother, especially if there are other young children at home. But one of the symptoms of

Figure 9.7a & b Sibling visiting the hospital at the earliest opportunity.

depression is lassitude, and it may be that effect and cause have been confused. The Dutch, who have a much higher proportion of home deliveries than is currently the case in United Kingdom have a Maternity Home Help Service. Trained home helpers not only assist domestically at the time of the delivery, but help with the running of the household for eight to ten days after the delivery. In the United Kingdom the Home Help service is less specifically trained. A young woman returning home with a baby after 10 days in hospital may face a dispiriting pile of dirty socks, a run-down food cupboard and forgotten rubbish bins. We would speculate that if more effort were expended in helping a woman to maintain her role in relation to other members of the family, and helping her retain control of her own environment the incidence of depression would go down.

Some fathers take annual leave from their work at the time their baby arrives, but paternity leave has not yet been as seriously considered as it should be. The full-time help of fathers for a week or fortnight around the baby's birth may be a factor facilitating early discharge, integrating the family, and giving much needed emotional support to the mother who can then better attend to the new baby. When she is at home she knows it is she who is responsible for the baby's welfare. Inevitably in hospital that responsibility is divided, which is not necessarily to the benefit of normal mothers with healthy babies.

Mothers sometimes have sleep problems. These may arise because their babies are night-wakers (see Ch. 2). It may have an endogenous origin in some worry, realistically based or otherwise. A midwife would be well advised to be cautious about a post-natal sleep problem and not to think immediately of narcotics. The post-natal period requires considerable adjustments to accommodate to a new role, to a new member of the family, to a new family. This cannot always be done overnight and with ease. There may be a lot of worrying to do. 'How will I manage . . . How is my husband going to like it when we both go home . . . How about the other children/my mother/my father . . . How am I going to like it?' As Brenda in *Saturday Night and Sunday Morning* says bitterly to her boyfriend when she discovers she is pregnant: 'What do you think having a kid means? . . . suddenly you're swelling. Then one fine day you're yelling out and you've got a kid. Nowt wrong wi'that. The thing is you've got to look after it every minute for fifteen years. You want to try it sometime.' (Sillitoe 1958).

If an opportunity is given to talk about things the midwife may be able to help a mother to think about things in a more constructive way. A few women are genuinely faced with the prospect of losing their husbands because they are jealous of the amount of time their wives spend with the baby. Barbiturates may induce an artificial sleep, create dependence and thereby assure the husband that he was right in thinking that the baby has made his wife neurotic, and the whole thing was a big mistake. A midwife may be able to listen sympathetically to the dilemma of such a patient. It is possible that husband and wife could discuss their problems together with the midwife. She may find she would need to refer the matter to a social worker who has a special understanding of family difficulties.

Many new mothers have no experience of babies and very little relevant information. There are a number of practical matters which may become greatly exaggerated in their minds, and which may not be difficult to set aright. Little things about their baby's appearance, to the midwife quite insignificant, can cause excessive worry. Many mothers, for example, are greatly concerned about forceps' marks on the baby's face, which is extremely unlikely to have anything but a very brief existence. The effects of episiotomy and perineal stitches, abdominal striae and so forth on their sex lives may bother them. Some factual information may be all that is required.

There are other reasons for being cautious about drugs in the puerperium. There is considerable public concern over the abuse and over-prescription of drugs including barbiturates (Matthew 1966). The increase in their use is brought about through overprescribing and recent evidence (Ghodse 1976) showed that barbiturates are now commonly used by multiple drug abusers. In addition, studies of sleep show that there are several different types or stages of sleep, character-ised by different patterns of brain activity, and other bodily change, all of which are essential to normal health. A drug-induced sleep has a different pattern from that of natural sleep, and alters the time spent in some stages at the expense of others. On waking, patients rarely feel refreshed as they would from natural sleep. The reason is believed to be that they are suffering deprivation of a particular stage of sleep, (Tune 1968).

We have already discussed the effects on their relationship, of either mother or baby being unresponsive. Not only is a mother who is taking barbiturates for sleeping likely to be drowsy, but if she is breast feeding the baby is likely to be affected.

Mothers are sometimes kept awake by their babies even when they are in hospital. Hospitals vary in the provisions they make for babies at night. Some stay with their mothers, others go to the nursery. Some babies are incorrigible night wakers, and the evidence is that it is futile to try to change them. Awkward as it may be for six or nine months, the solution for the mother may be to become a night waker with her infant and to try to organise her life to enable her to do this without too much strain.

It is obvious that sleep and rest which are proper for refreshment and recovery is essential in the puerperium. The effectiveness of drugs in this endeavour is questionable, and brings with it other problems. The measures suggested here might, with benefit, be tried first.

There are more serious and prolonged mental disturbances which can manifest themselves in the post natal period.

There is disagreement amongst psychiatrists as to the classification of psychoses related to childbearing, but psychoses in the first month after delivery are estimated to occur at the rate of 1 to 2 per 1,000 deliveries. A previous mental illness considerably increases the risk of recurrence, and this is far more likely to take place, if it does at all, in the post natal rather than in the antenatal phase.

Serious depression may result in withdrawal and detachment from the normal day to day interest of life. A pervasive black mood descends, making activity seem futile and every event is pessimistically interpreted.

Mania is the other major type of psychotic behaviour. Initially the patient may seem to be unusually ebullient. Jollity, endless activity, and talking continue unabated. The flow of ideas in the speech may become more and more disjointed, and activity destructive.

A schizophrenic episode is marked by disordered thinking, paranoia is not uncommon, and a seeming withdrawal of the patient into herself. Speech may become rambling, and the ideas that are expressed, may seem to have little relationship with one another. The style of the speech also fails to emphasise the emotional importance of its content. In normal speech we draw attention to the main features of our communication by the inflection of the voice; this is often missing in disordered speech.

An acute psychotic episode in the post-natal period may manifest itself by withdrawal and deep depression, paranoia, incongruous emotions and speech, or extreme excitability and activity. In the acute phase the infant is at risk and provision for his protection has to be made. In 1938 the murder of an infant under one year was made a special offence of infanticide, which is dealt with more leniently than murder. The court has to be satisfied that 'the balance of the mother's mind has been disturbed by reason of her not having fully recovered from the effect of giving birth to the child, or by reason of the effect of lactation consequent upon the birth' (Infanticide Act 1938). Giving evidence to the Royal Commission on the Treatment of Mentally Abnormal Offenders, the Governor and Staff of Holloway Prison had this to say:

> Most cases of child murder dealt with by the courts as infanticide are examples of the battered child syndrome in which the assault has had fatal consequences and the child is aged under 12 months. A combination of environmental stress and personality disorder with low frustration tolerance, are the usual aetiological factors in such cases, and the relationship to "incomplete recovery from the effects of childbirth or lactation" specified in the Infanticide Act is often somewhat remote. (Report of the Committee on Mentally Abnormal Offenders 1975.)

This serves to draw attention to situational factors which may contribute to any abnormal behaviour, a very small proportion of which is brought to public notice through the tragic event of a baby being killed by his mother. In 1974 thirteen women were proceded against for this offence in England and Wales (Criminal Statistics 1974). Such women are at the extreme of those who experience great difficulty in coping with the stresses and strains of life. Part of the stress and strain may well be endogenous but part, as the above extract makes clear, is in the conditions of living with which a woman is faced. These are conditions which can be ameliorated and with which the midwife may be able to help.

The patient will be referred to a psychiatrist and may be removed to a psychiatric unit. Until such specialist help is available the midwife has two important functions. One is to observe the patient's behaviour and make an accurate report about it, and the other is to maintain a high standard of care for mother and baby. The midwife, who is usually not psychiatrically trained, treats the mother with kindness and respect. This is reassuring to other patients who are likely to be alarmed. The common feature of psychotic behaviour is that it is not related to reality. The patient may become extremely agitated, threatened, or deeply depressed by a remark or an incident which seems unexceptional to anyone else. Abnormal reactions are more often the product of the patient's imagination however, and she may be deluded or hallucinated. Patients who have recovered from psychotic episodes recall them as extremely frightening and horrifying. It is useless, indeed sometimes dangerous, to try to persuade the patient that she is mistaken in her interpretation of events; it is likely to antagonise her and increase her paranoia. It may be helpful for her subsequent treatment if the midwife can observe whether there is any particular situation, or event, which causes the patient heightened distress. Because she perceives things in an abnormal way her actions are likely to be unpredictable and special care should be taken if she handles her baby. She may refuse to have anything to do with him, or claim that she has never had a baby, or attribute some inappropriate motivation to him. In the interim before she is seen by a psychiatrist, a major objective for the midwife is to *reduce the emotional temperature* and of course to prevent physical harm occurring. The matter will have to be discussed with the husband and possibly other relatives. If the mother is to be transferred to a psychiatric unit, some provision will have to be made for the baby, and this will involve the social worker who can discuss this aspect with the relatives. It is generally agreed that the baby should accompany the mother, and this is arranged wherever suitable facilities exist.

The other major concern with which midwives are increasingly faced in the post-natal period is contraception. There have been a number of developments in recent years which are likely to increase the involvement of midwives in family planning. The National Health Service (Family Planning) Act passed on 28th June 1967, enabled Local Authorities in England and Wales to provide a family planning service for all who want it. On 1st January 1975 contraceptive advice and supplies became available under the National Health Service, and on 1st October 1976 Area Health Authorities took over the statutory responsibility for making adequate provision. From 1st January 1976 family planning lectures, tutorials and clinic attendances became part of the midwives training and education, as laid down by the Central Midwives Board. As a result of recent legislation more hospital-based family planning clinics are likely to be established. The incorporation of this service into the National Health Service is likely to encourage discussion with mothers at any time during the pregnancy, but more particularly during the puerperium. This development occurring, as it does, concurrently with changes in the CMB syllabus, ensures that midwives will add fertility control to their interests and responsibility. A recent Government Working Party of 16 members, headed by Baroness Robson, has recommended that the nursing profession be empowered after suitable clinical training, to prescribe oral contraceptives for the normally healthy woman.

To some midwives the prospect of becoming involved in the technicalities of fertility control is distasteful. The early birth control clinics in this country were started by people motivated by a desire to see improvements in maternal and child health. It is only since the 1950's and the population *explosion* that the methods used to reduce the burden of large families and improve health and welfare, have been applied in some parts of the world to effect population control policies. The two should not be confused. Family planning involves the free choice and decision of a couple to time the arrival of their children, and to stop having babies when they have enough. They may choose to have none, or two, or twenty-two. Population control may not be possible on the basis of the personal choice of individual couples, as they may choose to have more than is compatible with population control or reduction.

Family planning, to be acceptable and effective, requires the support of other social and health services. In some parts of the world where population growth is very rapid, attempts to impose limitations on fertility have met with resistance. In India official targets are set for vasectomies to be performed. Some minor officials are reported to be over enthusiastic in trying to meet these targets, with inadequate consideration of the wishes of the local population. When the medical vasectomy team arrive by landrover they run the risk of being stoned. Many people living in underdeveloped countries still experience a fairly high infant and child mortality rate. Where this is the case, there is a strong motivation to have many children as an insurance for the parents old age, and to safeguard the inheritance of any property there may be. When a family planning service is not associated with maternal and child welfare, and some facilities for the care of the old, then it is likely to be unacceptable. There is a considerable difference for a midwife in being involved in advising couples who want information and guidance on family planning with a view to improving the quality of family life, and being involved in government schemes of population control.

Midwives and nurses may now choose to proceed to a special training course in family planning. Any midwife however, may be asked for advice about contraception in the post natal period. Many women at that time welcome the opportunity to discuss their own family planning needs and methods, and may be open to influence.

The normal procedure is that the earliest family planning consultation takes place after the post-natal examination, and that means six weeks, or perhaps more, after delivery.

A woman with her first baby, may never have organised any method of fertility control before the pregnancy. The under twenty age group is the only one in which the birth rate is not declining. Michael Schofield's study of the *Sexual Behaviour of Young People* (1965) showed how infrequently boys and girls between 13 and 19 took precautions to avoid conception, even when having frequent sexual intercourse. Some women who have been on the pill need to change their method of contraception for medical reasons. Intrauterine devices have to be re-inserted and cap size may need changing. Altogether a number of patients for a variety of reasons will have no immediate access to contraceptive advice, and no one with whom to discuss the matter for about six weeks.

It is a primary tenet of the family planning service that the only suitable method is that which is acceptable to both the partners. The technically ramshackle method of contraception with which a couple feel content, will be far more effective than the technically perfect system which is for some reason objectionable or distasteful. Large sums of money have been spent on research into inhibiting the biological process of reproduction, but remarkably little attention has so far been paid to the psycho-social factors which are generally acknowledged to be of the utmost importance when a couple come to make a decision about how to limit their fertility. Midwives have a great investment in reducing infant mortality and morbidity, and improving both child and parental health. To be maintained, these improvements have to be associated with effective fertility control.

In this country at present, between two thirds and three quarters of couples use contraceptive methods which are not doctor related (Wollf 1971, Cartwright 1970). This must surely give us some indication of attitudes to either doctors, or the methods they can make available. There is a variety of contraceptive methods; there are various ways in which these methods may be obtained; and the methods which do exist may require forethought or action by either husband or wife.

Any couple may have attitudes to the method, the means of provision, to each other, or to their own bodies which will affect acceptibility. Positive attitudes of provider and users to each other, and to the method, are necessary if any system is to work efficiently and smoothly. Some of the more technically advanced methods of fertility control are at present only available from a medical practitioner – that is someone specifically trained to deal with illness and disease. At the most vigorous and active stage of life there may be a considerable reluctance to seek advice from a doctor. Doctors are not only associated with illness and invalidity, but also enjoy high status and exercise considerable authority.

There is evidence that potential users of the family planning service desist from doing so because of their dislike of its association with medical formalities (Snowden and Grossmith 1975). Health professionals easily forget what intense foreboding a lay person has at the prospect of being medically examined. In some clinics the medical examination is taken as an opportunity to take a cervical smear. Desirable as this may be from a public health point of view, it is absolutely unrelated to family planning. There is also the very considerable inconvenience of visiting the doctor – often associated with frustrations of waiting. This involves either .time off work, finding a baby sitter, or taking the baby along.

The most commonly used methods of contraception are withdrawal and the sheath. The former requires no more than strong will power and the latter access to a slot machine. Withdrawal, in particular, is often not recognised as a method of birth control and is frequently referred to as *being careful.*

It will be apparent that the two methods already mentioned as being the most popular, are also male methods, although the sheath should be used in conjunction with a vaginal spermicidal pessary to maximise its effectiveness. Couples vary in their view as to who should take responsibility for their fertility control. Where the man is the leading partner, then the likelihood is that he will take effective responsibility in this matter as in other major matters of concern in the family. (An I.P.P.F. team in Iran dispensed pills to the women – after a few months only 12 per cent were still adhering to the scheme. The pills were then dispensed to the men to give to their wives. 92 per cent were continuing with the programme months later. In a male dominated society it was seen to be important that the men actually retain control over this important function.)

Some women believe that when they are breast feeding conception cannot occur, as they do not appreciate that ovulation occurs prior to the first post-natal menstrual flow. This is a misapprehension which the midwife is in a good position to dispel. She may also need to provide some factual information about the methods of contraception that are available, and places in the locality where they can be obtained.

Long-term advice cannot however be obtained before the post-natal examination. Abstention for that length of time is quite impracticable for most couples, who will be strongly motivated to snuggle down together without too much delay. There is no period of automatic security against a further pregnancy following delivery. Withdrawal is associated with rather high failure rates, so that leaves the condom with vaginal pessary as the best method to be used until more detailed family planning advice can be sought.

A patient may be concerned about the effects of perineal repair or abdominal scarring on the satisfaction of herself and her husband. Injuries to the pelvic floor which have been inexpertly repaired may lead to dyspareunia or to dissatisfactions caused by overstretched muscle and connective tissue. Abdominal scars are normally small and neat and are not disfiguring, although both partners may be very conscious of them in the first week or so. Difficulties may be experienced in returning to a normal pattern of sexual activity for psychological reasons. A woman who has had a difficult pregnancy, labour or delivery, and has been frightened or traumatised by excessive pain, may find her responsiveness dampened.

There is evidence that parents with handicapped children run a higher risk of separating than others. A handicapped child, of course, introduces a variety of strains and stresses into the family. He may, by causing some degree of depression in one or both parents, lower motivation, including sexual motivation. So far as we know, no studies of sexual problems following childbirth have examined this question, though no doubt in the case books of marriage guidance counsellors there is material which could verify or refute the hypothesis.

The human sexual co-ordination of a permanent partnership is a complex affair, involving all aspects of the personality, as well as physical synchrony.

The birth of the baby will change relationships in the family, and possibly occasion some personality development in both parents. The post-natal period is the time of rapid change making considerable demand on a woman's ability to adapt to her new role, new family and new self.

REFERENCES

Blake A., Stewart A, & Turcan, D. (1975) CIBA Foundation Symposium 33. *Elsevier Excepta Medica.*

Bowlby, J. (1969) *Attachment & Loss: I Attachment.* London: Hogarth Press.

Breen, Dana. (1975) *The Birth of a First Child.* London: Tavistock Publications.

Cartwright, Ann. (1970) *Parents & Family Planning Services.* London: Routledge & Kegan Paul Ltd.

Criminal Statistics, England & Wales (1974) Cmnd. 6168. London: HMSO.

Ghodse, A., Hamid. (1976) Drug problems dealt with by 62 London Casualty Departments. *British Journal of Preventive & Social Medicine,* **30**, No. 4 pp 251-256.

Harper, Rita F., Sia, Conception, Sokal, Sandra, Sokal, Myron. (1976) *Journal of Paediatrics,* **89**, No. 3. pp 441-445.

Klaus, H.M. & Kennell, J.H. (1979) Human Maternal Behaviour at first contact with her young. *Paediatrics,* **46** (2) pp 187-192.

Lynch, A.M. (1975) Ill health and child abuse. *Lancet,* **2**, pp 317.

Matthew, H. (1966) *British Medical Journal,* **2**, p. 298.

Moss, Howard A. (1967) Sex, age and state as determinents of mother-infant interaction. *Merrill Palmer Quarterly,* **13.** pp 19-36.

Prince, J., Firlej, M., Harvey, D. (in press). Contact between babies in incubators and their caretakers.

Report of the Committee on Mentally Abnormal Offenders (1975) Cmnd. 6244. London: HMSO.

Royal College of Midwives (1966) *Preparation for Parenthood.*

Schofield, M. (1965) The Sexual Behaviour of Young People. Harlow: Longmans.

Sillitoe, Alan. (1958) *Saturday Night & Sunday Morning.* London: W.H. Allen.

Snowden, N.R. & Grossmith, E.J. (1975) Contrasting Trials of use and provision of family planning services. *Journal of Family Planning Doctors,* **1**, No. 1, p. 1.

Tune, G.S. (1968) The Human Sleep Debt. *Science Journal,* **4** pp 67-71.

Wollf, Myra. (1971) *Family Intentions.* London: HMSO.

Yalom, I.D., Lumde, D.T., Moss, R.H., Hamburg, D.A. (1968) Post partum Blues Syndrome. *Archives of Genetic Psychiatry,* **18** (1) pp 16-27.

10

Going home

Patients are usually delighted to go home. After the gratitudes, the thanks, the words of advice the most important thing is to get home to independence, to be on one's own territory and to work things out. An additional member of a family alters its structure (that is the way members relate to each other). A first baby necessitates quite considerable adaptation in the relationship between husband and wife. Their concerns and conversations will change and their attention will be divided between the baby and their partner. This applies particularly to the mother who may find that the demands the baby makes necessarily reduce the time she can spend with her husband.

The second baby in turn alters a mother's relationship with both her husband and the first child. Jealousy is the likely outcome if attention which a person believes should rightly be theirs is diverted elsewhere. It is an emotion, by no means unheard of, in fathers of first babies and is almost universal in first children if the second born arrives at a critical stage of his development. Sewell (1930) found that jealousy in the first sibling is likely when the second baby is born when he is between 18 and 42 months. This is exactly the time when most families have their second baby. From a physiological and family planning point of view the spacing of two to three years has much to recommend it. Parents can perhaps be encouraged, before the new baby goes home, to pay special attention to the older child, or children, and to incorporate all members of the family in caring for the new baby (Fig. 10.1). The problem is specially acute when the second birth is a multiple one. The two and a half year old first born daughter of a family known to us was transformed from a reasonable and happy child to a murderous little virago when her twin siblings came home. Her mother had had to be in hospital for longer than usual. From the child's point of view she had been abandoned by her mother, who, when she eventually returned, devotedly attended to two hubristic miscreants. The emotional power generated by such an experience may remain a permanent feature, although it usually takes a more socially acceptable direction later in life. It is a circumstance which is difficult to cure but which much might be done to prevent by maintaining contact between mother and older child, keeping her informed, getting her to share the care of the babies, but otherwise minimising contact with them in her presence.

Figure 10.1. Older child being encouraged to join in.

Husbands who feel jealous can express their feelings and are aware of the source of their moodiness. Small children however cannot say what it is that angers them and they may become hostile and difficult to get on with. Not only are young children likely to be jealous of the new baby, but they can react badly to the mother's absence. If the mother has been in hospital for a week or ten days, and they were inadequately prepared for her departure, they may feel that she has abandoned them. When she returns, instead of being greeted by a welcoming little son or daughter, she may be given a very cold shoulder.

Young children separated from their mother can go through the stages of protest withdrawal and despair. The films made by James and Joyce Robertson of the Tavistock Clinic show this well, especially the film *John*. The separation can create in them a feeling of insecurity, which may show itself in clinging and demanding behaviour. The mother who goes home to a toddler, may find that she has to contend with a new baby and a child who has regressed in his social behaviour. The mother may find that she is put out, too, over a number of small things. She may find that the family have got on remarkably well without her. Instead of being welcomed into the vacuum that was left by her departure, she finds that people are tardy in making room for her. 'We've done it this way for the past ten days' her husband or her mother may say, as she settles into an accustomed task . . . or 'I've altered the furniture in the living room while you were away; you have been wanting it done for months.' She may be pleased the job is done, but regretful that it could be done without her.

A mother can also feel very possessive about her baby and resent the time her husband spends with him. Being a member of a family has problems as well as pleasures. The rearrangement of relationships that has to occur with a new member joining the family, may take a little while to sort out and will need patience. The number of potential relationships in a group multiplies rapidly as the number of members increases. A three person group can relate to each other like this:-

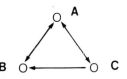

But A may also relate to B & C who act in unison on some matter.

Let us add two more people:-

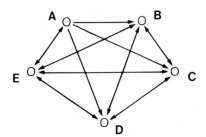

Each member can relate to every other individual. A however may sometimes have to deal with B C D & E combined, or B & C, and D & E and so on.

For those who like formulae here are two. The first one is the formula for calculating the number of single relationships and the second is more complex and gives in addition the possible ways members can group themselves and act in concert.

$$1. \quad x = \frac{n^2 - n}{2}$$

$$2. \quad x = \frac{3n - 2^{n+1} + 1}{2}$$

Where x = number of relationships

n = number of individuals

Table 10.1 shows the number of potential relationships there are in groups of different sizes.

Number of members	Simple one to one relationships (Formula 1)	Complex relationships (Formula 2)
2	1	1
3	3	6
4	6	25
5	10	90
6	15	301
7	21	966

Table 10.1

You will see that in addition to problems of jealousy, role change, and allocation of territory, the addition of say a third child, increases the potential number of relationships from 25 to 90 (Hare 1962).

There is considerable evidence that many first born children develop in rather different ways from subsequent children (Altus 1966, Sampson 1962, Bartlett and Smith 1966). First born children tend to be more independent and to be higher achievers. One of the explanations put forward for this is that the first born is the only child in a family who has his parents to himself for a period, and then has to share them. No matter how understanding the parents nor how much they may compensate to the first born the inescapable fact is that when the second baby arrives he experiences the loss of the undivided attention of his mother and father. One view about the first born, is that he can never again take the love of his parents for granted, but has to win their affection. The longing to be reinstated motivates the child to show how worthy he is of parental affection. This may become a permanent character trait, impelling him to achieve highly throughout life. First and only children are often expected to be more responsible than later born children in the family.

Another important factor with the first born is that it is generally the first experience for the parents with *any* baby. They therefore do a lot of learning, and perhaps make a lot of mistakes with the first one. Most parents would agree that they are more anxious with their first born. The mother may look at her sleeping baby every twenty or thirty minutes to assure herself that he is still breathing. When the second one arrives she is so much more confident and relaxed that she will not peer anxiously at him so frequently! Most parents remember a lot about their first baby – when he first sat up, spoke, walked, as well as innumerable amusing stories about his early adventures. With each successive member of the family, the details of the child's birth and development may be less and less precisely recalled.

In addition there is a higher rate of abnormality during the pregnancy, labour and delivery with first babies. This may mean that the first borns are in general rather more difficult children to manage.

Urban industrialised societies have predominantly a nuclear family structure. That is mother, father and children form an independent unit. The extended family consisting not only of mother, father and children, but grandparents, uncles and aunts, which characterises some of the less advanced societies, has a number of advantages for the new mother which we lack here in Britain. Children in extended families can experience multiple-mothering which releases the mother from the entire twenty-four hour a day responsibility for the care of her young. There is now appreciable evidence that many mothers of pre-school children are unable to enjoy the company of their youngsters on account of being depressed, socially isolated and miserable. From an active economic and social life, many have to adapt to financial dependence and severe social limitations. Despite sentimental attitudes, the mother role is not highly valued in this society, which takes its measure from more specifically task directed roles. Many people, especially men, when asked who they are describe themselves in terms of a task: 'I am a bus driver', 'I am a teacher' but full-time mothers will often say 'I am only a mum'. 'I am *only* . . . ' is a denigrating self assessment.

Mothers who are more positive about their role (as they often are if they have a challenge to deal with e.g. a handicapped child) occasionally find themselves compelled to assert their position vis a vis the specialist teacher, pediatrician, health visitor, and social worker. There is no specific training for motherhood as there is for bus driving and teaching. In the specialisation which occurs with advance in society, parenting has been left out, and is done well or ill on the basis of casual labour. A few voices have been raised in a plea for parentcraft classes for both boys and girls from school days onward. So far however such classes are rather casual and *ad hoc*.

We have a society of one family units, where work is quite separate from the home, in which motherhood is not a highly regarded task. In some urban areas the position for mothers is made worse by the architectural lunacy of having people live on top of one another instead of side by side. We talk to people whom we meet face to face, not people who live *above* or *below* us. In consequence a very common complaint by the mothers of young children, is that they are lonely, bored, depressed, stuck-at-home and unfulfilled. Not the ideal atmosphere for a baby to develop into a joyful, exploring, curious, bright and interested child.

A midwife cannot alter our nuclear family structure nor the architecture of the towns. There is much that mothers can do in the way of self help and the midwife may be in a good position to make relevant suggestions. Young mothers groups are sometimes based on the local health visitors' clinic. They may meet to discuss common problems, to exchange children's clothes and equipment, and deal with a variety of practical and social matters. A few mothers can combine to form a babysitting group so that each member can leave her baby for a couple of hours with someone who is known, and who will become a firm acquaintance of the child as well. In some areas the Local Authority or the Workers' Educational Association run classes in the morning or afternoon with a crêche attached. Classes on a wide range of topics can often be arranged in response to a specific request by a local group. The absence of stimulation both social and intellectual, can be sorely felt. Boredom and isolation have their effects, not only by making people *feel* dreary; they have a disabling effect on thinking, on psycho-motor skills, on the ability to plan and think ahead and indeed affect the whole personality. A guiding word from the midwife which will encourage the new mother to think what active steps she can take to combat these risks may have permanent value.

The mother who comes from a cohesive family is specially fortunate. She can look forward to sharing the experience of caring for the baby with her husband and may also have help from her mother who can build up her confidence. The problem of the grandmother usurping the mother's role is a well-known one. This may be a special risk if grandmother has recently retired from a job, or lost her husband, or for some other reason is making a new role for herself.

Some others will be going home without the help and support of a husband. We have discussed in Chapter 7 important differences between being unmarried and unsupported. What matters to mother and baby is that they can return to a home where care and affection are shown. Some patients cannot look forward to such a welcome. A baby brought up without a permanent male figure in the house may be at a long-term disadvantage. His mother, however, needs some supportive person as soon as she leaves hospital. Looking after a young baby is not an easy job for the inexperienced and untutored. In addition the unsupported mother is likely to have worries about practical matters that a more fortunate woman is spared. Despite more liberal attitudes, having a baby without an identifiable male support is socially disapproved. Probably the only exception to this is the woman whose husband has died during the pregnancy. A woman on her own, needs to be exceptionally capable to make provision for her children in a way that would compare with the two-parent family.

The single mother may be resentful, guilty or bereft at being on her own. She may be afflicted with many doubts about her relationships and her competence. However satisfactorily she comes to terms with events, caring for a young child single handed is a further strain. She should be referred to the social worker before she goes home, so that every form of support available can be offered.

The mother with the handicapped child may have to go home before her baby is fit enough to be discharged from hospital. This in itself is a problem. Is she a mother or not? One of the requirements of the mother role is that the baby should be cared for. If she is not competent to care for him, she forefeits the role. The precariousness of the infant's status affects hers, and for the time until her baby can come home she is likely to be in a state of limbo. Much of the time in hospital will have been devoted to considering the prospects for the baby and making plans for the future. The parents, in their relationships with staff, may have begun to adjust to the idea of having a child with a handicap. Once at home the whole process has to be gone through again with neighbours and friends. If the handicap is perceived as a minor one an attitude of guarded optimism and encouragement for the new mother may prevail. Many parents have found that the embarrassment of a major handicapping condition serves only to turn them in upon themselves. Neighbours do not speak because they do not know what to say. Neither rejoicing nor commiseration seem appropriate. The parents' response of not initiating contact is predictable, and they run the serious risk of becoming more and more socially isolated. This may have a souring effect on them, and hinder the child's prospects of development.

The midwife may be able to discuss these problems with the mother before she goes home. The prospects for the individual child can never be predicted with absolute accuracy. While it would be irresponsible and unkind to encourage false optimism, it is quite realistic to press the view that whatever the child's handicap his chances of developing his potential can best be helped by the provision of social and mental stimulation by affectionate parents. In practical terms this means taking him to the shops, and to visit friends, talking and playing with him, providing him with play things, and later on playmates. A mother of a child with a handicap should be encouraged to view her baby as the repository of unknown potential which she has the important function of helping him to discover. The ratio of disappointment and frustration to joy and achievement, may be different from that with a normal child. The maintenace of the parents' own social lives is of great importance too, if they are to avoid an accumulation of the stresses imposed by a handicap in the family.

Some mothers are so distressed at the prospect of living with a handicapped child that they abandon him to the hospital from whence he must sooner or later be transferred to the care of the Local Authority. It is undoubtedly right that the community generally should take a share in the disproportionate demands made by a child with a serious disability. If community support can be effectively channelled through the parents, the benefits to the child can be inestimable. The fact that some parents do abandon their children, is a measure of the failure, as the parents see it, of the community to make its supportive services clearly available.

The health visitor has a duty to visit parents of pre-school children after they leave the care of the midwife. It is to the health visitor that the parents may turn for help and advice in the early days at home. Before leaving hospital the mother is given an appointment for a postnatal check. In addition to these universally available services, we give below some addresses of organisations which may be of help to parents for themselves, and in connection with special problems they may have with their babies (see p. 171-2).

REFERENCES

Altus, W.D. (1966) Birth Order and its sequelae. *Science,* **151** 44-49.
Bartlett, E.W. & Smith, C.P. (1966) Child rearing practices, birth order and the development of achievement related motives. *Psychological Reports,* **18** 1207-1216.
Hare, A. Paul. (1962) *Handbook of Small Group Research.* London: Collier MacMillan Ltd.
Sampson, E.E. (1962) Birth order, need achievement and conformity. *Journal of Abnormal and Social Psychology,* **64** 155-159.
Sewell, M. (1930) Some causes of jealousy in young children. *Study of Social Work,* **1** 23-40.

11

The future

The midwife role envisaged in this book builds on the traditional one in a number of ways.

Professional tasks change: that of the midwife has changed in the past ten years more rapidly than most. There are two major reasons for this. One is obstetric and political decisions which have actually altered the sphere of influence of the midwife. The other is an increasing interest in the psycho-social factors affecting mothers, babies and families.

The midwife occupies a lynch-pin position in the maternity and child welfare services, and how she interprets her role is likely to affect associated professions, and the quality of family life. It may not exaggerate the case to say that practising midwives are now at the crossroads, and the route they take will affect not only their own profession but the kind of society we shall have in the future. The nature of human beings is to a considerable extent shaped by their early experience. Decisions concerning childbirth, in so far as they affect the early experience, will affect the society of the future. They also affect women vitally. They are the people who have babies and take major responsibility for their care. Until 1977 midwifery was also an exclusively female profession.

The process of childbirth has been changed dramatically by obstetric decision which is now being reassessed. 'A re-analysis of the situation now suggests that the technique (induction of labour) is not as good as we thought it would be' Professor Turnbull, Nuffield Professor of Obstetrics, said at a recent medical conference (1976).

'It is becoming clear that indiscriminate hospitalisation, which undoubtedly decreases risks attached to childbirth for a few, when applied to the many serves only to increase risk for them overall' (Tew, 1977). 'One hundred per cent hospital delivery means an increased risk of death for the majority of mothers and babies' (Watkin 1977).

Patients' associations of various kinds have been publicising evidence on the effects of current obstetric practice and attempting to effect changes.

Jean Donnison has traced in exquisite detail the relations between the medical profession and the *women's business* of attendance at childbirth in her book *Midwives and Medical Men. A History of Interprofessional Rivalries and women's rights.* 'We have yet to see', she says in the penultimate paragraph of the book 'whether the new militancy of the women's movement will prompt British women to take the stand on home deliveries taken by some of their American sisters'. If they do, will there be a domiciliary midwifery service left for them to call upon? 'Domiciliary midwives were one of the most popular services the NHS provided and had the highest consumer rating under the local authorities' it was claimed at a Royal Society of Health Conference at Eastbourne in May 1977. Since the reorganisation of the health service the duty of appointing domiciliary midwives which was vested in the Local Authority has not been imposed upon Area Health Authorities.

Midwives have been proud to proclaim that they are practitioners in their own right, and CMB rules lay down with some precision the area of their autonomy, and the conditions and situations where medical aid is to be summoned. There is no doubt that their area of autonomy has been greatly eroded in the past few years. If this is to the benefit of mothers and babies there can be no cause for regret. If, as now seems possible, the benefits to some are bought at the cost of detriment to others, a modification of present procedure may be called for. 'Early transfer to the care of community midwives, and general practitioners after delivery, is already increasingly in demand.' (Allen 1977).

The monopoly control of goods or services is not highly regarded in Britain, and strenuous attempts are made to avoid or break monopolies. There is little reason to believe that a hundred per cent hospital delivery system will be any more welcome, or more efficient than any other monopoly control. In other areas of the health and social services there is increasing emphasis on community care and self-help. Great effort is expended on maintaining patients at home, and educating them and their families to greater independence. The concern with community care has arisen in response to changes in patterns of illness, and in the age structure of the population. An important influence affecting the matter has also come from the recognition that human beings are adversely affected in health and happiness when they are moved from their familiar territory. Individuals in large groups, where they feel themselves to be insignificant, often become depressed, lethargic, feel helpless and generally lack motivation.

These are some of the reasons why there is now increasing emphasis on community nursing. The Community Psychiatric Nurse with special training and qualification has a responsibility for looking after the psychiatric patient in his own home and for supporting his family. A recent report on District Nurse education and training advocates an extended and obligatory training. These developments are a response to the need for domiciliary care, and a recognition of the special requirements of the practitioner in the community. It is an anomaly that the work of midwives, who have traditionally been community based, and whose skills have been held in high regard, have found their work being removed from community to hospital, and their domicilliary skills allowed to wither through lack of practice.

The term *community* is illdefined but is generally taken to refer in this context, to a particular geographical area which is characterised by a more or less common set of values, ideas and attitudes, customs and traditions, in work and leisure.

It is the family in the community with which most community health workers have dealings. The emphasis on the family was re-iterated by the Court Report (*Fit for the Future* 1976) 'We want to see a child and family centred service. . . '

The midwife is the professional person who has been most intimately concerned with the family at those critical family building times when its members are changing and developing, and when it is most in need of counsel and support. The value of the intimate caring concern of a single identifiable person can hardly be overestimated. Yet it is this very person who, against public expressions of concern about family welfare and expansion of other community services, is on the verge of extinction.

The midwife living and working in the community has the opportunity not only to know individual families well, but to understand their ethnic or class *milieu*. Areas are well or badly provided with services. The local midwife who knows the area can be adept at facilitating the use of voluntary and other services which do exist. She is likely to know families with teenage boys and girls, who may be willing to help with some shopping or with the toddler. She will know who has a pram or baby clothes for sale, who can spend a couple of hours gardening or helping with housework. This facilitating role which midwives have played can be very important to the young pregnant woman or the mother with a new baby who feels isolated and depressed.

Community work needs the best qualified and most experienced workers. It is not hospital work done in less hygenic surroundings. All the technical skills learned in hospital are necessary, and in addition a comprehension of different cultural and class values and attitudes, an appreciation of the interaction within families, a knowledge of local resources and facilities, considerable inner strength, flexibility and self-confidence. A hospital is very supportive to its staff as responsibility is widely shared and decisions rarely need to be made without consultation.

If, as seems likely, midwifery in the United Kingdom is to be affected by our membership of the European Economic Community, one of the immediate concerns will be the quality of training. In some countries of Europe midwives have longer training, enjoy greater public esteem, and have a deeper knowledge of their subject than is the case in the United Kingdom. Parity of education and training will be required if there is to be parity of opportunity in employment. As will have been made clear from this book, we think there is a great need for an improved understanding of the social and behavioural sciences in midwifery. Above all, the midwife needs the self-confidence, which usually comes with improved education, to be absolutely clear what midwifery is, what her role is, and how it relates to other professional tasks.

Walker (1976) in an enquiry into the perception of the role of the midwife by midwives and obstetricians found that 'in general, there is a confusion among doctors and midwives as to the role of the midwife'. In her sample of 49 midwives and 11 obstetricians all agreed that the midwife should be responsible for normal antenatal care, labour and delivery, and the obstetrician for any abnormality occurring at any time during that period. The areas of confusion were those where responsibilities overlapped and had not been clarified – such as antenatal care, and assessment of mother's and infant's condition after delivery.

We would argue that there are nursing needs and a nursing process with which it should be the job of the trained nurse to assess and deal; that there are midwifery needs and processes with which it should be the job of the trained midwife to assess and deal; that there are medical needs and processes with which it should be the job of the doctor to deal. The day has long passed when all aspects of care could be understood and administered by one person. Doctors, like most other professional people, have to contend with a great volume of scientific data relevant to their work, and must make decisions on matters relating to their medical competence. Nurses are now recognising the fact that there is a nursing process which is related to but independent of the medical one and for which they must be responsible and make decisions. Midwives, if they are to survive as an independent professional body, must recognise the fact also, that there is a midwifery process, arising out of normal pregnancy, labour and puerperium, distinct from the obstetric process and they must be prepared to make midwifery decisions and to be fully aware of the bounds of their knowledge and skill.

'If only we could regain our confidence in the normality of the great majority of women, and leave them to the care of midwives and husbands, then there would be ample time to put the remaining 20 per cent under the obstetrical microscope.' *Dunn 1976*

The appropriate use of midwifery skills depends very largely on good antenatal supervision, and refinement in the perception of factors related to high risk.

Another impetus to a reconsideration of the present position comes from the accumulating material on the socio-psychological criteria of good maternity and baby care which is the main subject matter of this book. Maternity care is not the only area where an exclusive concern with medical criteria has been found wanting. Physical events are inevitably associated with psychological ones, and disproportionate concern with one aspect at the expense of the other is rarely to the patient's advantage. The concern of midwives with the normal maternalizatum can only be effectively demonstrated if they keep abreast of all relevant scientific developments, which now includes the social sciences, as well as the more traditional topics.

Many physical factors are not difficult to measure. Whether a baby is dead or alive is usually obvious; whether he has respiratory distress, or is jaundiced, may need a more skilled eye but essentially the problem is concrete and 'pointable-at'. Whether a mother feels good about her baby and can encourage his development appropriately, or whether she feels distant from him, or that he is just hard work, is not so easy for an observer to appreciate. This is only likely to be revealed to, or recognised by, someone who has prolonged contact and a good relationship with the mother. The consequences may be long term and quite as weighty as physical events. Many a child with Down's syndrome, who is loved and accepted as he is, lives a happier and more fulfilled life than the physically normal child whose personality is distorted by negligence, indifference, or excessive demands for achievement.

The physical, social and emotional conditions in which children are conceived, carried, born, fed and nurtured contribute to the moulding of their personalities, and affect the families into which they are born. Midwives have a distinctive and irreplaceable contribution to make to this vital developmental stage. They have long been recognised as competent to deal with the physical aspects of normal pregnancy, labour and puerperium, and many practising midwives will from their experience, have developed intuitive insights beyond much of what we have written. We hope however that this book may help to clarify the basis of their understanding. We hope too, that future midwives and parents may have sufficient confidence in themselves to make their appropriate contribution to the childbearing process. It is an event of critical importance to the life of the child, to the next generation and to the society of the future.

REFERENCES

Allen, June E. (1977) Home deliveries: A challenge. *Nursing Mirror,* **144** No. 11. p 43.

Donnison, J. (1977) *Midwives and Medical Men.* London: Heinemann.

Dunn, Peter M. (1976) Obstetric delivery today. For better or for worse. *The Lancet,* **1** pp 790-793.

Fit for the Future (1976) The Report of the Committee on Child Health Services. London: HMSO.

Tew, Marjorie. (1977) Where to be born. *New Society.* **39** No. 746 pp 120-121.

Turnbull, A. (1976) Proceedings of the British, Canadian and Irish Medical Associations at their Conference in Dublin.

Walker, Jean F. (1976) Midwife or Obstetric Nurse. *Journal of Advanced Nursing Studies,* **1** pp 129-138.

Watkin, Brian. (1977) *Nursing Mirror,* **144** No. 8 pp 42.

Where to look for help for parents and their young children

This list is very short. Their are many organisations, both statutory and voluntary set up to deal with specific and general needs. These few suggestions we hope will provide ideas as to where to begin.

General

Statutory services The general practitioner and health visitor work within the Area Health Authority. There addresses and telephone numbers can be found in the telephone book or from the local town hall.

The social worker is an employee of the Local Authority and can be contacted in the same way.

For single parents

'Gingerbread', 9, Poland Street, London W1V 3D9 – there are local branches which provide social contacts and activities for parents and their children.

National Council for One-Parent Families, 255, Kentish Town Road, NW5 2LX. Telephone: 01-267-1361. Works for the welfare of one parent families by giving advice on legal and financial matters, offering a counselling service and working for improvement in the services.

For the family with a handicapped child

An invaluable source of information will be found in *A handbook for Parents with a Handicapped Child* by Judith Stone and Felicity Taylor, published by Arrow Books Ltd, 1977.

Association for Spina Bifida and Hydrocephalus, 30 Devonshire Street, London W1N 2EB. Telephone: 01-486-6100, and has 70 local associations.

Downs Babies Association, Quinborne Community Centre, Ridgacre Road, Birmingham B32 2TW. Telephone: 021-427-1374.

Invalid Children's Aid Association, 126 Buckingham Palace Road, London, SW1 9SB. Telephone: 01-730-9891.

Spastics Society, 12 Park Crescent, London W1N 4EQ. Telephone: 01-636-5020.

Toy Libraries Association, Sunley House, 10 Gunthorpe Street, London E1 7RW. Telephone: 01-247-1386/7.

For the family with a gifted child

National Association for Gifted Children, 27 John Adam Street, London WC2 6HX.

For the parents

Workers Educational Association, 9 Upper Berkeley Street, London W1 H8B. Telephone: 01-402-5608. The WEA have local branches in most parts of the country. Morning or afternoon classes, with creche facilities, are run where there is local demand, although most of the educational work is done in evening classes.

National Housewives Register, c/o Josephine Jaffray, Holmshaw, Moffat, Dumfrieshire. DE10 9SQ. Telephone: Beattock 422. For women who can develop activities including paid work, from their own homes.

Women's Rights Campaign, Flat 2, Menelik Road, London NW2. Telephone: 01-794-950.

Patients' Association, Suffolk House, Banbury Road, Oxford. Telephone: Oxford 50306. The only association which represents the views of patients in the National Health Service.

For the pregnant woman

Association for Improvement in the Maternity Services, 21 Iver Lane, Iver, Bucks. Telephone: Iver 652781.

National Childbirth Trust, 9 Queensborough Terrace, London W2. Telephone: 01-229-9319. An educational charity providing antenatal preparation for parents, help with breast feeding, as well as seminars and study days.

Foundation for Education and Research in Childbearing, 27 Walpole Street, London S.W.3. Telephone: 01-235-1343. Disseminates information on all aspects of childbearing.

National Birthday Trust, 57 Lower Belgrave Street, SW1. Telephone: 01-730-7392. Initiates and supports research into aspects affecting maternal welfare.

Index